Neapolitan Boy

Painted by the Italian artist ANTONIO MANCINI

3

The World of Music

RHYTHMS AND RIMES

ENLARGED EDITION

By

MABELLE GLENN

DIRECTOR OF MUSIC, PUBLIC SCHOOLS, KANSAS CITY, MISSOURI

HELEN S. LEAVITT

INSTRUCTOR IN MUSIC, BOSTON UNIVERSITY AND THE WHEELOCK SCHOOL
BOSTON, MASSACHUSETTS

VICTOR L. F. REBMANN

FORMERLY DIRECTOR OF MUSIC, WESTCHESTER COUNTY, NEW YORK

EARL L. BAKER

FORMERLY DIRECTOR OF PUBLIC SCHOOL MUSIC DEPARTMENT
LAWRENCE COLLEGE, APPLETON, WISCONSIN

ART EDITOR

C. VALENTINE KIRBY

STATE DIRECTOR OF ART EDUCATION, PENNSYLVANIA

GINN AND COMPANY

BOSTON · NEW YORK · CHICAGO · LONDON · ATLANTA · DALLAS · COLUMBUS · SAN FRANCISCO

The World of Music

KINDERGARTEN	ELEMENTARY GRADES	ALL GRADES
SING A SONG	LISTEN AND SING	SINGING DAYS
PLAY A TUNE	TUNING UP	
	RHYTHMS AND RIMES	
	SONGS OF MANY LANDS	
	BLENDING VOICES	
	TUNES AND HARMONIES	

Classified Contents

Classified Contents

There are here 106 folk songs and 47 composed songs.

Rote Experience: 40 rote songs, indicated by the word ROTE under the title.

Music Reading: 113 songs; review of elements previously presented; introduction of eighth notes.

All the songs in this book correlate with the child's studies, interest, and experience.

Reproductions of Noted Pictures: Neapolitan Boy, *Antonio Mancini*, frontispiece; Chums, *Francis C. Jones*, 19; Indian Harvest, *Eanger I. Couse*, 38; Whistling Boy, *Frank Duveneck*, 55; Feeding Her Birds, *Jean François Millet*, 106; Infant Samuel Praying, *Sir Joshua Reynolds*, 123; Girl with Cat, *Paul Hoecker*, 142; The Santa Fe Trail, *John Young-Hunter*, 159.

Songs of American Life

The early settlers of this country were simple men and women who brought with them the folk traditions of their native land. The New World offered so little culture and recreation that they clung to their national inheritance of song and story and passed it on to their children and to their children's children.

Gradually the folk songs of these people became a part of our American life. So songs from countries across the seas came to express the life of pioneer America and were sung by the builders of our great country. Through generations these familiar airs have come down to us by oral repetition.

Like echoes from long ago, many of the songs on the following pages are our musical heritage, and they will continue to be a significant influence on the growth of America.

No. 1 · We're All Americans
No. 2 · Paper of Pins
No. 3 · High, Betty Martin
No. 4 · Deep in the Forest
No. 5 · The Ballit of the Boll Weevil
No. 6 · A Long Time Ago

No. 7 · When Johnny Comes Marching Home
No. 8 · Levee Song
No. 9 · The Railroad Corral
No. 10 · The Star-Spangled Banner
No. 11 · Old Noah, He Did Build an Ark

No. 12 · Work, for the Night is Coming
No. 13 · Snake Dance Song
No. 14 · Oh! Susanna
No. 15 · Old MacDonald Had a Farm

No. 1. We're All Americans[1]

Words and music by
James T. Mangan

We're all A - mer - i - cans! · We're proud to

bear the name, · Our na - tion's fa - thers wove a flag

· By the light of free - dom's flame, · Now wav - ing

brave - ly o - ver - head, · It tells us what to do, ·

We're all A - mer - i - cans! · All True Blue. ·

No. 2. Paper of Pins

This is an old, old song which has become very popular in the United States. The gift of a paper of pins meant a great deal more in olden days than it does now. Even a single pin was something to be prized, and an offer of a paper of pins almost equaled that of a pearl necklace nowadays.

For a long time Americans have sung it, clapped hands and tapped heels to it, at play parties all over the South and West, in the mountains and on the plains.

Traditional

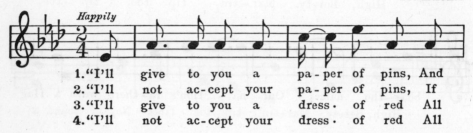

1. "I'll give to you a pa- per of pins, And
2. "I'll not ac- cept your pa- per of pins, If
3. "I'll give to you a dress. of red All
4. "I'll not ac- cept your dress. of red All

that's the way my love be- gins, If you will mar- ry
that's the way your love be- gins, And I'll not mar- ry
bound. round with gold- en thread, If you will mar- ry
bound. round with gold- en thread, And I'll not mar- ry

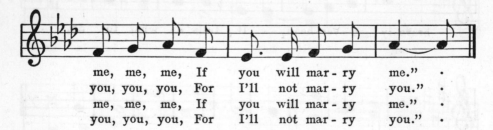

me, me, me, If you will mar- ry me." .
you, you, you, For I'll not mar- ry you." .
me, me, me, If you will mar- ry me." .
you, you, you, For I'll not mar- ry you." .

5. "I'll give to you the key to my heart,
That you and I may never part,
If you will marry me, me, me,
If you will marry me."

6. "I will accept the key to your heart,
That you and I may never part,
And I will marry you, you, you,
And I will marry you."

No. 3. High, Betty Martin[1]

This is a fiddle tune that was sung and danced at many of the country dances.

American Traditional

High, Bet-ty Mar - tin, tip toe, tip toe,

High, Bet-ty Mar-tin, tip toe fine. Nev-er found a

man to suit her fan - cy, Nev-er found a

man to suit her mind. Tra la la la

la la la la, Tra la la la la la la la,

8c

High, Betty Martin (*Continued*)

Tra la la la Bet-ty Mar-tin, Tip toe fine.

No. 4. Deep in the Forest[1]

The ancient Ojibway Indians who lived north of Lakes Huron and Superior used to have a ceremony that took place at daybreak, and this song was an important part of it. In recent years the Ojibways have sung this melody with different words, but in the English version we have kept to the original idea.

Ethel Crowninshield   Ojibway Indian

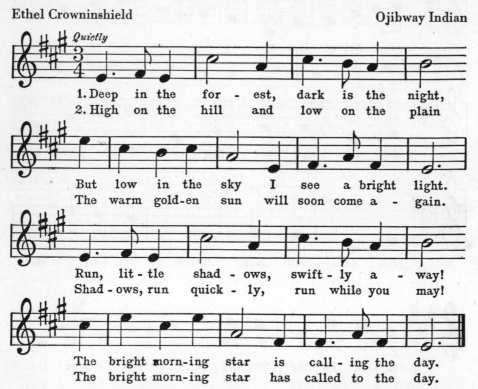

Quietly

1. Deep in the for - est, dark is the night,
2. High on the hill and low on the plain

But low in the sky I see a bright light.
The warm gold-en sun will soon come a - gain.

Run, lit - tle shad - ows, swift - ly a - way!
Shad - ows, run quick - ly, run while you may!

The bright morn-ing star is call - ing the day.
The bright morn-ing star has called to the day.

[1] From *American Primitive Music*, by Frederick Burton, published by Moffat, Yard and Company, 1908.

No. 5. The Ballit of the Boll Weevil

A boll weevil is a little bug that gets in the flower-like cotton ball on a stalk of cotton and eats it. A "ballit" is a ballad and a ballad is a song-story. Do you know of any other crops that suffer heavy losses from insects?

Ballad from Texas

1. The boll wee-vil is a lit-tle black bug From Mex-i-co they say, Come to try the Tex-as soil, And he thought he'd bet-ter stay, Just a-look-ing for a home,
2. The first time I see the boll-wee-vil He was sit-ting on the square; And the next time when I see him He had all his fam-i-ly there, Just a-look-ing for a home,
3. The farm-er took the boll-wee-vil And put him in the sand; And the boll wee-vil said to the farm-er, "I'll stand it like a man, For it is my home,
4. The farm-er took the boll-wee-vil And left him on the ice; Said the boll wee-vil to the farm-er, "This is might-y cool and nice, It is my home,

8e

The Ballit of the Boll Weevil (*Continued*)

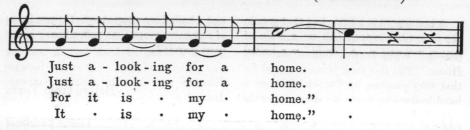

Just a - look - ing for a home.
Just a - look - ing for a home.
For it is my home."
It is my home."

No. 6. A Long Time Ago[1]

Sometimes the word "chanty" is spelled "shanty." A chanty is a work song of the sailor which he often sings in rhythm with his body as he works aboard ship. It is easy to imagine that this one might have been used when pulling on the ropes.

With spirit — Sea Chanty

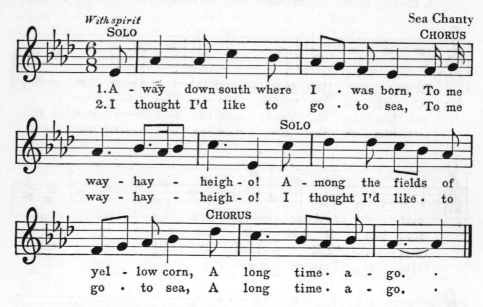

SOLO CHORUS

1. A - way down south where I was born, To me
2. I thought I'd like to go to sea, To me

SOLO

way - hay - heigh - o! A - mong the fields of
way - hay - heigh - o! I thought I'd like to

CHORUS

yel - low corn, A long time a - go.
go to sea, A long time a - go.

3. Around Cape Horn we've got to go
To me way-hay-heigh-o!
Around Cape Horn to Cal-la-o
A long time ago.

4. Around Cape Horn with frozen sails
To me way-hay-heigh-o!
Around Cape Horn to fish for whales
A long time ago.

[1]From *Folk Songs of Old New England*, copyright, 1939, by The Macmillan Company. Used by permission of Eloise Hubbard Linscott.

No. 7. When Johnny Comes Marching Home

When the soldier boys came home from the Civil War, they were welcomed by the tune of "When Johnny Comes Marching Home." For this song was composed for that very purpose by Patrick Gilmore, a band leader who wrote his songs under the name of Louis Lambert. This is one of the gayest, happiest songs Americans sing. It has a touch of Irish feeling, and we can understand that very easily because Gilmore was born in County Galway, Ireland.

Louis Lambert

With spirit

1. When John-ny comes march-ing home a-gain, Hur-rah, · hur-rah! · We'll give him a heart-y wel-come then, Hur-rah, · hur-rah! · The men will cheer, the boys will shout, The

2. The old church bell will peal with joy, Hur-rah, · hur-rah! · To wel-come home our dar-ling boy, Hur-rah, · hur-rah! · The vil-lage lads · and las-sies gay With

3. Get read-y for the Ju-bi-lee, Hur-rah, · hur-rah! · We'll give the he-ro three times three, Hur-rah, · hur-rah! · The lau-rel wreath is read-y now To

When Johnny Comes Marching Home (*Continued*)

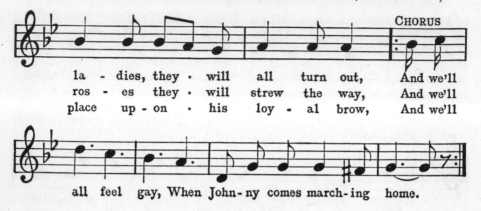

CHORUS

la - dies, they . will all turn out, And we'll
ros - es they . will strew the way, And we'll
place up - on . his loy - al brow, And we'll

all feel gay, When John - ny comes march-ing home.

No. 8. Levee Song

High banks are built along the lower Mississippi to keep the river from overflowing when the water is high. Steamboats tie up beside the levee, and a line of dock workers and stevedores march onto the boat, up on the levee and down on the boat, round and round, carrying freight on their backs and singing in rhythm to their walk and work. In his work as in his play the Negro always sings.

American Traditional

With expression

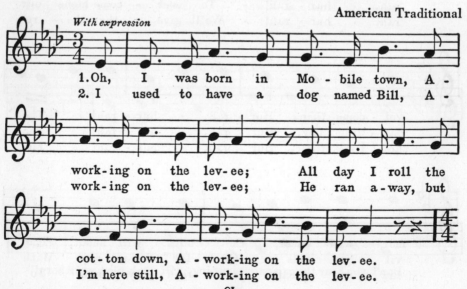

1.Oh, I was born in Mo - bile town, A-
2. I used to have a dog named Bill, A-

work-ing on the lev-ee; All day I roll the
work-ing on the lev-ee; He ran a-way, but

cot - ton down, A - work-ing on the lev-ee.
I'm here still, A - work-ing on the lev-ee.

8h

Levee Song (*Continued*)

I've been work-ing on the rail - road All the live - long

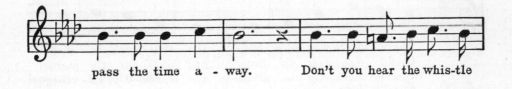

day; I've been work-ing on the rail - road, To

pass the time a - way. Don't you hear the whis-tle

blow - ing, Rise up so ear-ly in the morn;

Don't you hear the cap-tain shout-ing, "Di - nah, blow your horn!"

No. 9. The Railroad Corral

The words of this song give a clear picture of the long drive to the railroad. A big corral for the cattle is built by the railroad siding. The cattle are driven from the different pens that make up the corral, up a long chute into a cattle car. The door is fastened and the car is attached to a freight train and goes on its way to market. These cattle cars have slatted sides so that there is more air for the animals.

This song should be sung with a light, galloping rhythm.

Song of the Cowboy

1. We're up in the morn-ing ere break-ing of day,
2. Come, take up your cinch-es, come, shake out your reins,
3. The · aft-er-noon shad-ows are start-ing to lean
4. But the long-est of days must reach eve-ning at last,

The · chuck wag-on's bus-y, the flap-jack's in play.
Come, wake your old bron-co and break for the plains;
When the chuck wag-on sticks in the marsh-y ra-vine;
The · hills · all climbed, the creeks · all passed;

The herd is a-stir o-ver hill-side and vale,
Come, roust out your steers from the long chap-ar-ral,
The herds scat-ter far-ther than vi-sion can look,
The tired · herd droops in the yel-low-ing light,

With the night rid-ers crowd-ing them in-to the trail.
For the out-fit is off to the rail-road cor-ral.
You can bet all true punch-ers will help out the cook.
Let them droop if they will, for the rail-road's in sight!

8j

No. 10. The Star-Spangled Banner

Francis Scott Key

John Stafford Smith

1. Oh, · say! can you see, · by the dawn's ear - ly light,.
2. On the shore, dim - ly seen · through the mists of the deep,
3. Oh, · thus be it ev - er when · free - men shall stand

What so proud - ly we hailed at the twi - light's last
Where the foe's haugh - ty host in dread si - lence re -
Be - tween their loved homes and the war's des - o -

gleam-ing, Whose broad stripes and bright stars, through the per - il - ous
pos-es, What is that which the breeze, o'er the tow - er - ing
la - tion! Blest with vic - t'ry and peace, may the Heav'n-res-cued

fight, O'er the ram - parts we watched were so gal - lant - ly
steep, As it fit - ful - ly blows, half con-ceals, half dis -
land Praise the Pow'r that hath made and pre-served us a

stream-ing? And the rock-ets' red glare, the bombs burst-ing in
clos - es? Now it catch-es the gleam of the morn-ing's first
na - tion! Then con - quer we must, when our cause it is

The Star-Spangled Banner (*Continued*)

air, Gave proof through the night that our flag was still there.
beam, In full glo - ry re - flect-ed, now · shines on the stream.
just, And this be our mot-to: "In · God is our trust!"

Oh, · say does that Star-span-gled Ban - ner yet wave
'Tis the Star-span-gled Ban-ner: oh, long may it · wave
And the Star-span-gled Ban-ner in tri - umph shall wave

1, 2, 3. O'er the land · of the free and the home of the brave?

No. 11. Old Noah, He Did Build an Ark

College Song

With spirit

1. Old No - ah, he did build an ark, He made it
He drove the an - imals two by two, The ele - phant
2. And when he found he had no sail He just ran
And then he nailed the hatch - es down And told out-

Old Noah, He Did Build an Ark (*Continued*)

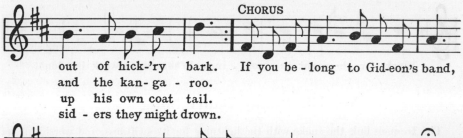

CHORUS

out   of hick-'ry   bark.   If you be - long   to Gid-eon's band,
and   the kan- ga - roo.
up   his own coat   tail.
sid - ers they might drown.

Why, here's my heart and here's my hand, Look-ing for a home.

3. Full forty days he sailed around
And then he ran the ark aground.
He landed on Mount Ararat
Just three miles south of Barnegat.

No. 12. Work, for the Night is Coming

This serious song was written just at the close of the Civil War, when Americans were tired of death and battle, and brother fighting against brother. The feeling of the nearness of death and the shortness of life hovers over this strange song like a black cloud. It is a warning to work and live *now*, for the moments to live are few.

Annie L. Walker

Lowell Mason

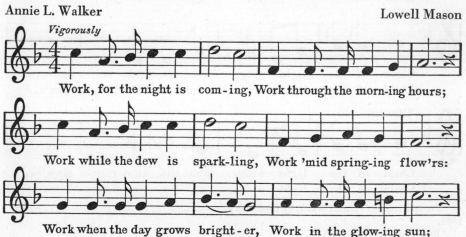

Vigorously

Work, for the night is   com-ing, Work through the morn-ing hours;

Work while the dew is   spark-ling, Work 'mid spring-ing flow'rs:

Work when the day grows   bright - er, Work in the glow-ing sun;

Work, for the Night is Coming (*Continued*)

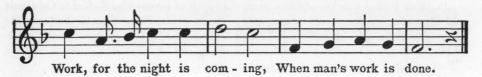

Work, for the night is com - ing, When man's work is done.

No. 13. Snake Dance Song[1]

The Iroquois link the snake with the lightning for its swiftness, and worship it for its wisdom.

Christine Turner Curtis   Iroquois Indian Song

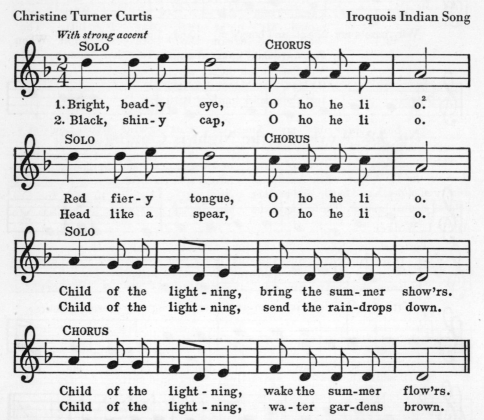

With strong accent

SOLO ... CHORUS

1. Bright, bead-y eye, O ho he li o.[2]
2. Black, shin-y cap, O ho he li o.

SOLO ... CHORUS

Red fier-y tongue, O ho he li o.
Head like a spear, O ho he li o.

SOLO

Child of the light - ning, bring the sum-mer show'rs.
Child of the light - ning, send the rain-drops down.

CHORUS

Child of the light - ning, wake the sum-mer flow'rs.
Child of the light - ning, wa-ter gar-dens brown.

[1] From *American Primitive Music*, by Frederick Burton, published by Moffat, Yard and Company, 1908.

[2] Pronounced ō hō hā lē ō.

No. 14. Oh! Susanna

Stephen Foster was twenty-two years old when this, his first song-hit, was sung all over America. The "Forty-niners" sang it all the way to California the next year. "Forty-niners" was the name given to the crowds of people who flocked to California to get gold. From then on Foster wrote songs for a livelihood because the popularity of "Oh! Susanna" proved that the public liked his songs.

Stephen C. Foster

Stephen C. Foster

Lively

1. I · came from Al - a - ba - ma, With my ban - jo on my knee, I'm gwine to Lou - si - an - a My · true love for to see; It ·

2. I · had a dream the oth - er night When ev - 'ry-thing was still, I · thought I saw Su - san - na A - com-ing down the hill; The

rained all night the day I left, The weath - er it was dry, The sun so hot I froze to death, Su - san - na, don't you cry.

buck - wheat cake was in her mouth, The tear was in her eye; Says I, "I'm com-ing from the South, Su - san - na, don't you cry.

CHORUS

Oh, Su - san - na, oh, don't you cry for me, I've come from Al - a - ba-ma with my ban-jo on my knee.

No. 15. Old MacDonald Had a Farm

The animals on Old MacDonald's farm, and the length of this song, are only limited by the amount of imagination and enthusiasm of the singers. Usually this song appears early on the programs for community singing because the "E-I-E-I-O's" and imitations of different animal noises add a note of informality that breaks down the shyness of even the most timid person.

Traditional

In merry mood

1, 2, 3. Old Mac-Don-ald had a farm, E - I - E - I - O!

1. And on this farm he had some chicks, E - I - E - I - O!
2. And on this farm he had some ducks, E - I - E - I - O!
3. And on this farm he had some tur-keys, E - I - E - I - O!

With a chick, chick, here, and a chick, chick, there,
With a quack, quack, here, and a quack, quack, there,
With a gob-ble, gob-ble, here, and a gob-ble, gob-ble, there,

Here a chick, there a chick, ev-'ry-where a chick, chick.
Here a quack, there a quack, ev-'ry-where a quack, quack.
Here a gob-ble, there a gob-ble, ev-'ry-where a gob-ble, gob-ble.

1, 2, 3. Old Mac-Don-ald had a farm, E - I - E - I - O!

8p

Night and Day

**After the original by
Louise Ayres Garnett**

ROTE

Yugoslavian Folk Song

1. When a - bove the sun - set gold - en glow
2. Do you think the moon has had to say,

The sil - ver stars be - gin to show,
"Get up and lay your dreams a - way;

Do you won - der how they al - ways know
For the night is yours to work and play

It is time to light the sky?
As the sleep - ing world goes by."

9

How Do You Do?

ROTE

Louise Kessler

Austrian Folk Tune

1. In the leaf-y tree-tops the birds sing, "Good morn-ing."
2. In my pret-ty gar-den the flow-ers are nod-ding.

They're first to see the sun;
"How do you do?" they say,

They must tell ev-'ry-one;
"How do you do to-day?"

In the leaf-y tree-tops the birds sing, "Good morn-ing."
In my pret-ty gar-den the flow-ers are nod-ding.

A Little Bird

English version by
Rose Fyleman

ROTE

Yugoslavian Folk Song

Happily

1. A lit - tle bird sat up - on a tree;
2. I looked at him, and he looked at me;

I looked at him, then he looked at me.
I gath - ered straw - ber - ries, one, two, three.

Be - low him there in my gar - den bed
But I have not an - y doubt, have you,

Were shin - ing straw - ber - ries ripe and red.
That lit - tle bird, he will get some, too?

Uncle Frank

ROTE

Monica Shannon

G. A. Grant-Schaefer

Not too fast

1. It's queer a - bout my Un - cle Frank;
2. Or he might keep a big toy - shop

He sits and fig - ures in a bank,
With things that fly and skip and hop,

When he might keep a can - dy store,
With trail - er trucks and things that crank,

A shin - y sign a - bove the door.
In - stead of work - ing in a bank.

Cradle Song

ROTE

Anonymous

Tenderly

German Folk Song[1]

1. Sleep, ba - by, sleep. Thy fa-ther tends the sheep;
2. Sleep, ba - by, sleep. And you shall have a · sheep,

Thy moth - er shakes the dream-land tree,
And he shall have a gold - en bell

And down come all the dreams for thee.
And play with ba - by in the dell.

Sleep, ba - by, sleep.
Sleep, ba - by, sleep.

[1] This is No. 11 of the German folk songs which Brahms arranged for the children of Robert Schumann.

13

Young Mister Duck

Mabel Livingstone   ROTE   Victor Young

1ST VOICE 1. "Quack, quack, quack! What shall I do?
　　　　　2. "Quack, quack, quack! If I should try,

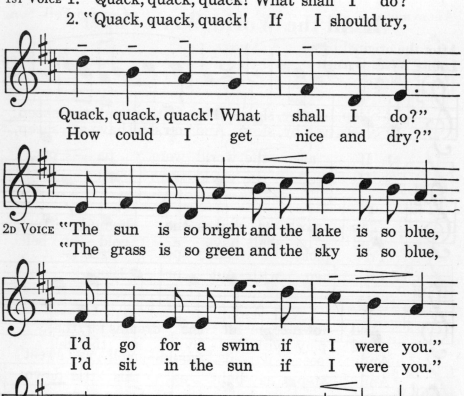

Quack, quack, quack! What shall I do?"
How could I get nice and dry?"

2D VOICE "The sun is so bright and the lake is so blue,
　　　　　"The grass is so green and the sky is so blue,

I'd go for a swim if I were you."
I'd sit in the sun if I were you."

1ST VOICE "I've on - ly been swim-ming once or twice;
　　　　　"I've on - ly been swim-ming once or twice;

Quack, quack, quack! That would be nice."
Quack, quack, quack! That's good ad - vice."

If All the World Were Paper

After the original by
Louise Ayres Garnett

ROTE

English Folk Song

Merrily

1. If all the world were pa - per,
2. If all the world were pa - per,

I'd pick a pa - per rose, · ·
I'd go with - out my shoes, · ·

And see if it would smell as sweet
And step as light as this - tle-down

To an - y - bod - y's nose. ·
Each morn - ing in the dews. ·

October Days

Hope Ann Rhodes

Austrian Folk Tune

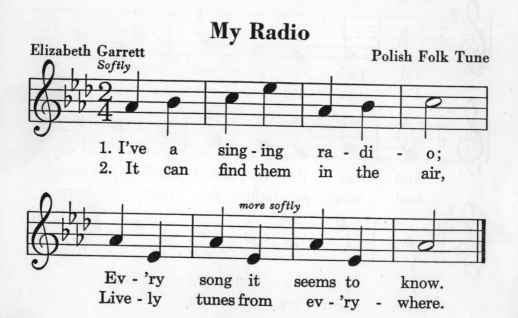

1. How we love Oc - to - ber days,
2. Car - pets bright on coun - try ways,

Red and gold and yel - low.
Ap - ples grow - ing mel - low.

My Radio

Elizabeth Garrett

Polish Folk Tune

Softly

1. I've a sing - ing ra - di - o;
2. It can find them in the air,

more softly

Ev - 'ry song it seems to know.
Live - ly tunes from ev - 'ry - where.

Birds and Fishes

Ethel Crowninshield

Austrian Folk Tune

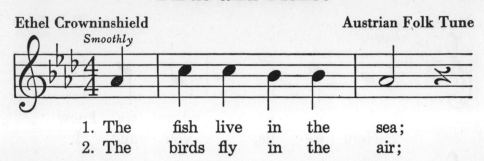

1. The fish live in the sea;
2. The birds fly in the air;

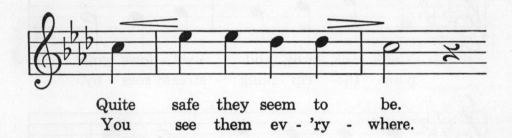

Quite safe they seem to be.
You see them ev - 'ry - where.

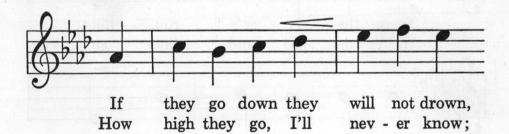

If they go down they will not drown,
How high they go, I'll nev - er know;

But that's no help to me.
I'd fly, but do not dare.

Chums

Marjorie Knapp   Austrian Folk Tune

1. Let us go where we know
2. Here we lie, you and I,

Cat - tails, ferns, and wil - lows grow.
While the rip - pling stream goes by.

There the riv - er's run - ning;
Watch your rod and line, sir!

There the frogs are sun - ning.
Keep it clear of mine, sir!

We can find the sport we wish.
Not a sin - gle bite to - day!

That's the fin - est place to fish.
All the fish must be a - way.

Chums

Painted by the American artist FRANCIS C. JONES, and now in a private collection

The Art Extension Press, Inc.

A Warning

ROTE

Loughlin-Knapp   Melba Knaus Loughlin

1. Rob-in,   rob-in,   sing-ing in the ap-ple tree,
2. Rob-in,   rob-in,   when the snow of win-ter flies,

Rob-in,   rob-in,   you are all a-lone, I   see.
Rob-in,   rob-in,   you will leave for south-ern skies.

Don't you know that sum-mer is   o - ver and   done?
Wait no long - er, rob - in, but   be on the   wing!

Bet - ter spread your wings and fly off to meet the   sun.
You will be   re - turn - ing to us a - gain in spring.

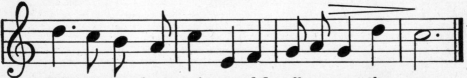

Bet-ter spread your wings and fly off to meet the   sun.
You will be   re - turn - ing to us a - gain in spring.

The Eskimos

Ethel Crowninshield   Austrian Folk Tune

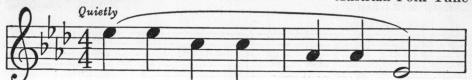

1. Far a - way in ice and snows
2. Stand - ing by their hous - es low,

Live the lit - tle Es - ki - mos;
Dressed in fur from head to toe,

Ver - y strange and queer they look
It has al - ways seemed to me

On the pag - es of my book.
Win - ter In - dians they must be.

3

A Scottish Tale

After the Scotch by
Nancy Byrd Turner

Scotch Folk Song

Lightly

1. A lad and las - sie ran a - way
2. If you will wan - der down the glen,
3. They live a - mong the fair - y folk,

One rol - lick - ing, frol - ick - ing wind - y day;
The heath - er - y, feath - er - y, mist - y glen,
The dear lit - tle, queer lit - tle fair - y folk.

The wind blew hard, the wind blew fast,
You'll find them if you find the way
Some - day a wind may sweep the glen

And blew them far from home at last.
They went that whirl - y, twirl - y day.
And blow them safe - ly home a - gain.

Mister Squirrel

Hope Ann Rhodes

Flemish Folk Tune

1. Mis - ter Squir - rel,   as you look for
2. Mis - ter Squir - rel bur - ies lots of

nuts   in   a   tree,
nuts   in the fall.

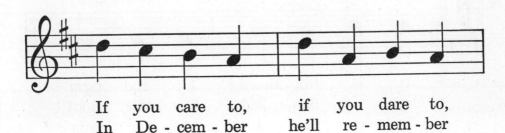

If you care to,   if you dare to,
In De - cem - ber he'll re - mem - ber

Get your nuts from me!
Where he put them all.

Out in the Country

Ethel Crowninshield   Austrian Folk Tune

1. 'Way out in the coun - try
2. Walk - ing near the barn - yard,
3. Tur - keys, geese, and chick - ens,

I shall spend the day;
Hear the roost - er crow,
Cows and hors - es too;

It is fun down on the farm,
"Cock - a - doo - dle, doo - dle doo!"
Ev - 'ry time I come a - gain

There is so much room to play.
Strut - ting proud - ly to and fro.
There is al - ways some - thing new.

Hi-ya Hi!

Translated by
Cecil Cowdrey

Hungarian Folk Song

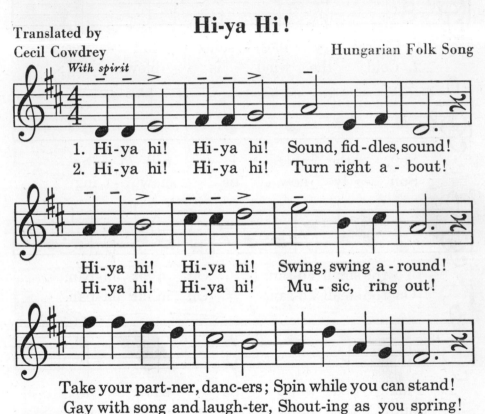

With spirit

1. Hi-ya hi! Hi-ya hi! Sound, fid-dles, sound!
2. Hi-ya hi! Hi-ya hi! Turn right a - bout!

Hi-ya hi! Hi-ya hi! Swing, swing a - round!
Hi-ya hi! Hi-ya hi! Mu - sic, ring out!

Take your part-ner, danc-ers; Spin while you can stand!
Gay with song and laugh-ter, Shout-ing as you spring!

Round and round, round and round, Spin hand in hand!
Round and round, round and round, Swing, danc-ers, swing!

Yo-San

ROTE

Fanny Giralda Pheatt   Fanny Giralda Pheatt

1. Cher - ry blos - soms fall - ing;
2. Cold the wind is blow - ing;

Soft the breeze is call - ing
Soft - ly now 'tis snow - ing

To the small Yo-san, · Off in far Ja-pan. ·
On the small Yo-san, · Off in far Ja-pan. ·

Pink and white 'tis snow - ing,
South the birds are fly - ing;

On the flow - ers grow - ing,
Dead the flow'rs are ly - ing,

In her qui - et gar - den,
In the qui - et gar - den

Off in far Ja - pan. · · ·
Of the small Yo - san. · · ·

Halloween

Moiselle Renstrom

Mysteriously

ROTE

Moiselle Renstrom

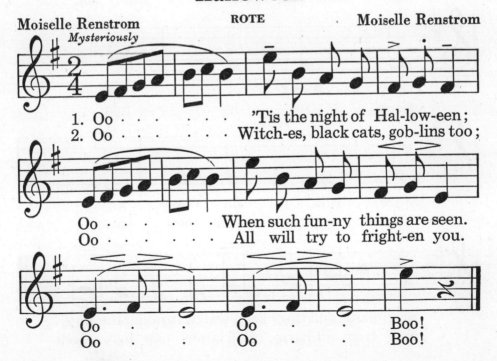

1. Oo · · · · · · · 'Tis the night of Hal-low-een;
2. Oo · · · · · · · Witch-es, black cats, gob-lins too;

Oo · · · · · · When such fun-ny things are seen.
Oo · · · · · · All will try to fright-en you.

Oo · · · · Oo · · · Boo!
Oo · · · · Oo · · · Boo!

Mountain Pastures

After the original by
Louise Kessler

French Folk Song

Quietly

1. Shad - ows of night
2. When all the sky

Curl up - ward in the dawn - ing;
Re - flects the crim - son sun - set,

Gray flocks of sheep
Back to the fold

Move slow - ly on their way;
The shep - herds bring their sheep;

Shep-herds and dogs keep watch through the day.
Safe from all harm, small lambs now may sleep.

Wild Geese

English version by
Louise Kessler

German Folk Song

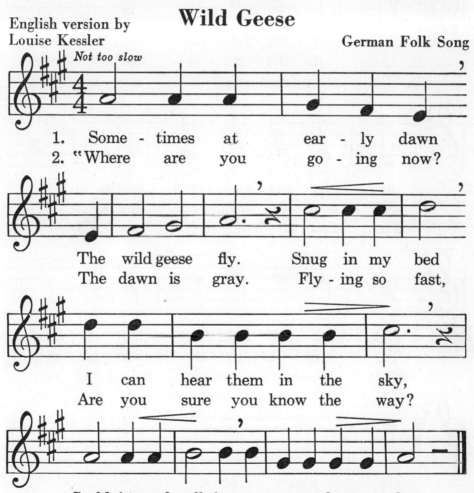

1. Some - times at ear - ly dawn
2. "Where are you go - ing now?

The wild geese fly. Snug in my bed
The dawn is gray. Fly - ing so fast,

I can hear them in the sky,
Are you sure you know the way?

Scold-ing and call-ing to me as they pass by.
Will you be call-ing on me some oth-er day?"

Johnny Stare

English version by
Cecil Cowdrey

Danish Folk Song

Merrily

1. When lit - tle John - ny went to school,
2. Once to the riv - er bank he went
3. Two strong men tried to get him out,

At bird and sky he'd stare—oh!
So near, a - las, so near—oh!
The fish they laughed for glee —oh!

But for the road that lay a - head
Till plunk! In - to the wa - ter cold
While John - ny's school bag, bright and new,

He took no care.
Fell John ny dear.
Sailed off to sea.

Pay with a Smile

After the original by
Ethel Crowninshield

ROTE

Irish Folk Song

With tenderness

1. Down to the riv-er came lit-tle Ei-leen
2. "If you cross o-ver the riv-er to-day,"
3. "Blue are your eyes and your smile is so bright;

With her bright gold-en hair like the crown of a queen.
Said the lad in the boat, "Why, you sure-ly must pay."
Since you ask me to take you, I'm sure it's all right.

For it's o-ver the riv-er to mar-ket she'd go,
"But I have-n't a pen-ny; I've walked for a mile;
So we'll hur-ry to mar-ket be-fore it can rain,

And she'll bring back a bun-ny that's white as the snow.
Yet, if you'll take me o-ver, I'll give you a smile."
And per-haps, if you ask me, I'll take you a-gain."

Shoes and Rubbers

Hope Ann Rhodes

Hungarian Folk Tune

Happily

1. Shoes or rub - bers, you'll a - gree,
2. Left and right they have to go,

An - y way you take them,
As their sides are curv - ing.

Look a - like, — but then, you see,
Turn them o - ver, then you'll know,

Left and right they make them.
If you are ob - serv - ing.

The Violin and the Drum

Beatrice Wadhams

Polish Folk Tune

In jolly mood

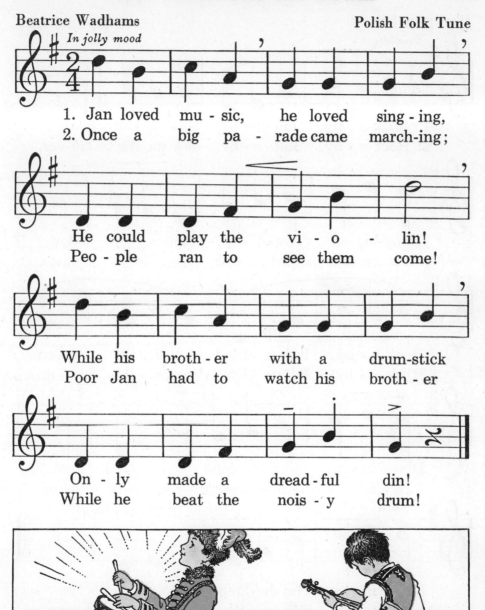

1. Jan loved mu - sic, he loved sing - ing,
2. Once a big pa - rade came march-ing;

He could play the vi - o - lin!
Peo - ple ran to see them come!

While his broth - er with a drum-stick
Poor Jan had to watch his broth - er

On - ly made a dread - ful din!
While he beat the nois - y drum!

Rock-a-by

J. G. Holland

Clara Edwards

Dreamily

1. Rock-a - by, lull - a - by, bees in the clo-ver,
2. Rock-a - by, lull - a - by, dew on the clo-ver,

Croon-ing so drow-si - ly, sigh-ing so low,
Dew on the eyes that will spar-kle at dawn,

Rock-a - by, lull - a - by, dear lit - tle rov - er,
Rock-a - by, lull - a - by, dear lit - tle rov - er,

Down in - to won-der-land go, now go,
In - to the still - y world gone, now gone,

Softer

Down in - to won-der-land, rock - a - by go.
In - to the still - y, the lil - y world gone.

On Columbus Day

Nancy Byrd Turner   Netherlands Folk Tune

With simplicity

1. We all are prais-ing Co - lum-bus to - day,
2. We all are prais-ing Co - lum-bus to - day,

That brave young dream-er who lived far a - way.
That strong young sail - or who sailed far a - way;

Day-time and night-time he nev - er could rest,
Guard-ing his dream as the storm - y winds blew,

Think-ing and dream-ing of lands in the west.
Watch-ing and hop - ing un - til it came true.

To Market

Louise Kessler   Lithuanian Folk Tune

1. Come, lit-tle po - ny, we must go to mar-ket!
2. Come, lit-tle po - ny, home-ward we are go - ing!

In the ear-ly morn-ing, we must go to mar-ket.
Ver-y late at eve-ning, home-ward we are go - ing.

Jig - gle, jog - gle, down the moun-tain,
Jig - gle, jog - gle, up the moun tain,

Jig - gle, jog - gle, down the moun-tain,
Jig - gle, jog - gle, up the moun-tain,

Thus we go to mar - ket.
Home - ward we are go - ing.

Elizabeth Garrett   Austrian Folk Tune

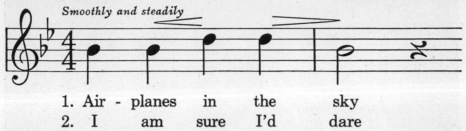

1. Air - planes   in   the   sky
2. I   am   sure I'd   dare

Each   day   are   roar - ing   by;
To   fly   high   in   the   air;

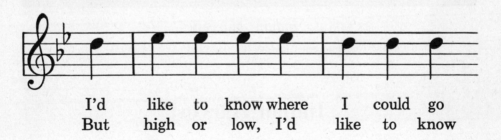

I'd   like   to   know where   I   could   go
But   high   or   low, I'd   like   to   know

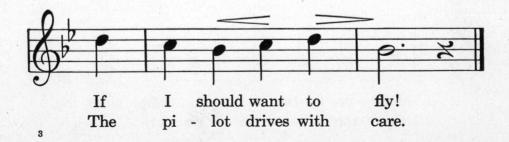

If   I   should want   to   fly!
The   pi - lot   drives with   care.

Indian Harvest

Painted by the American artist EANGER I. COUSE, and now in a private collection

Indian Harvest

Ethel Crowninshield   Traditional American

Slowly and rather seriously

1. Moth - er Earth, to   you we're sing - ing,
2. On   the trail where   we are   go - ing,

Lis - ten to our song!
Ev - er will wo sing!

Thanks for gold - en har - vests bring - ing,
When the win - ter comes with snow - ing,

Lis - ten as we sing to you!
Still our hearts will sing to you!

Softer

Sing to you! sing to you!
Sing to you! sing to you!

Slowly, with emphasis

Songs of rain and sun - shine!
Songs of rain and sun - shine!

3

Market Day

After the original by
Louise Kessler

Polish Folk Song

With spirit

1. Come, lad, the day a - wak - ens!
2. We'll sell some rye and bar - ley,

We'll make an ear - ly start.
Fine wheat and may - be hay,

There stand the pa - tient hors - es;
Five geese and twen - ty chick - ens;

Come, lad, and load the cart!
Hi - o, for mar - ket day!

Here and There

Louise Ayres Garnett

Spanish Folk Tune

1ST VOICE   In Spain, is it true 'tis sum-mer-time too?

Are clouds just as snow-y, are skies just as blue?

2D VOICE The same sun is shin-ing, the stars are not new,

And chil-dren are dream-ing the sleep-y hours through;

Per - haps some-one's sing-ing this song, just like you.

A Sea Lullaby

ROTE

Ann Flint

Mary Root Kern

With expression

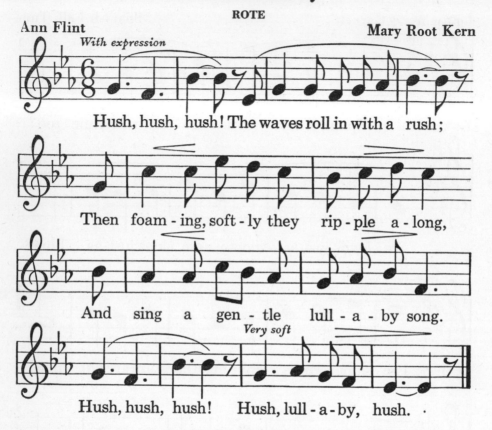

Hush, hush, hush! The waves roll in with a rush;

Then foam - ing, soft - ly they rip - ple a - long,

And sing a gen - tle lull - a - by song.

Very soft

Hush, hush, hush! Hush, lull - a - by, hush.

Thanksgiving

Ethel Crowninshield

Austrian Folk Tune

Brightly

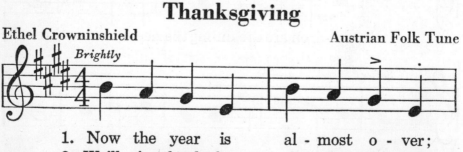

1. Now the year is al - most o - ver;
2. We'll give thanks for all the bless - ings

Here   is   No - vem - ber.
Each   day   has   brought   us.

Then   comes Thanks - giv - ing   Day,
Grate - ful   for   ev - 'ry - thing

Day   we   all   re - mem - ber.
That   the   year   has   taught   us.

Moon in the Sky

Moiselle Renstrom   Moiselle Renstrom

1. Moon,   moon,   up   in   the   sky,
2. Moon,   moon,   up   in   the   sky,

O   moon,   moon,   sail - ing on   high,
O   moon,   moon,   sail - ing on   high,

O   moon,   moon,   your sil - ver   light
O   moon,   moon,   where do you   stay

Can make the world love - ly   at   night.
When sun-shine turns night in - to   day?

Cats and Dogs

A NONSENSE SONG

Virginia Lynd Hartley

Czech Folk Tune

Playfully

1ST VOICE 1. Oh, my cat is pink,
2. Oh, my dog is green,

She likes play - ing in the ink!
He can count to sev - en - teen!

2D VOICE Oh, my cat is blue;
Oh, my dog is red;

She drinks cof - fee with her stew!
He eats pick - les with his bread!

Sky at Night

Sigmund Spaeth

Yugoslavian Folk Tune

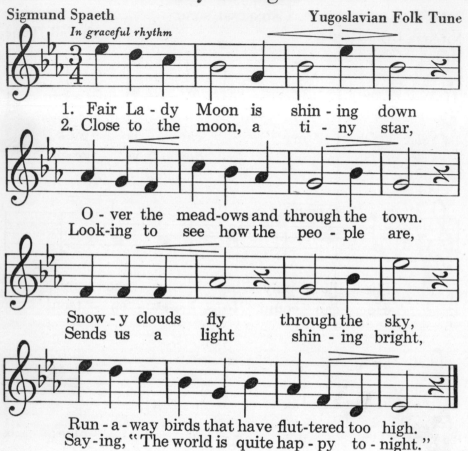

1. Fair La - dy Moon is shin - ing down
2. Close to the moon, a ti - ny star,

O - ver the mead-ows and through the town.
Look-ing to see how the peo - ple are,

Snow - y clouds fly through the sky,
Sends us a light shin - ing bright,

Run - a - way birds that have flut-tered too high.
Say-ing, "The world is quite hap - py to - night."

Learning to Drive

Carol Fuller

Otto Nicolai

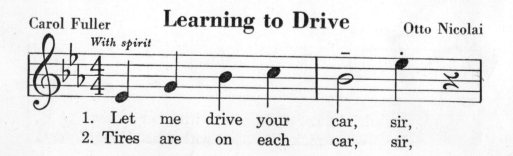

1. Let me drive your car, sir,
2. Tires are on each car, sir,

Learning to Drive (*Continued*)

Ver - y   fast   and   far,   sir!
Man - y   kinds   there   are,   sir!

Wait   a   mo - ment   while   I   learn
See,   I   real - ly   know   so   much.

How   to   stop   and   when   to   turn;
Where's   the   brake   and   what's   the   clutch?

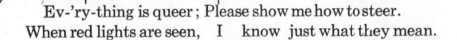

Ev-'ry-thing is queer; Please show me how to steer.
When red lights are seen,   I   know just what they mean.

Laughing Ho, Ho!

Carol Fuller   ROTE   French Folk Tune

1. We met a mouse who hat - ed cheese,
2. We own a la - zy ra - di - o,
3. We have a roost - er tall and white,

He was so hard to please.
That nev - er wants to go.
Who likes to crow all night.

Mous - ie, ho, ho! Ah, ha, ha, ha!
Ra - di - o, ho! Ah, ha, ha, ha!
Roost - er, ho, ho! Ah, ha, ha, ha!

Oh, what a fun - ny mouse you are, you are!
Oh, what a ra - di - o you are, you are!
Oh, what a nois - y bird you are, you are!

A Song of the Flag

Rebecca B. Foresman

Czechoslovakian Folk Tune

Slowly, with strong rhythm

1. Come, let us re - mem-ber as we sing to - day
2. There's a mes-sage that the flag brings ev-'ry-one,

Ev - 'ry flag we see would like to   say,
When we   see it wav - ing in the   sun;

"Men have spent their lives in work-ing hard for oth-ers;
Pass - ing by, let   us sa -lute our shin-ing col-ors,

So a trib-ute   to their mem-'ry we will   pay."
For they tell us   of the deeds brave men have done.

Things I Like Best

Ethel Crowninshield

Wolfgang Amadeus Mozart

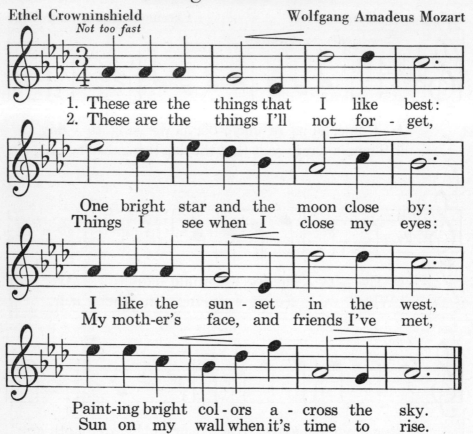

1. These are the things that I like best:
2. These are the things I'll not for - get,

One bright star and the moon close by;
Things I see when I close my eyes:

I like the sun - set in the west,
My moth-er's face, and friends I've met,

Paint-ing bright col - ors a - cross the sky.
Sun on my wall when it's time to rise.

Armistice Day

M. Louise Baum

Czechoslovakian Folk Tune

1. Let the bells be sound - ing
2. May our hap - py coun - try

Clear from ev - 'ry stee - ple,
Live at peace with oth - ers,

Ring - ing in the Peace Day
True to right and jus - tice,

God has giv'n the peo - ple.
Know - ing all as broth - ers.

The Harvest Festival

English version by
Maud W. Niedermeyer

Swiss Folk Song

Happily

1. Come dance with me, Ro - set - ta,
Swing right, swing left to - geth - er,
2. Here comes our friend Vi - net - ti
Per - haps we'll have a par - ty

Let me take your hand;
Then a curt - sy grand.
From a - cross the way;
On this hap - py day.

It is a mer - ry time of year;
He has a pitch - er and a cup,

D.C. al Fine [1]

The har - vest fes - ti - val is here.
He's call - ing us to hur - ry up;

[1] This means " go back to the beginning and end on ' Fine.' "

Names

ROTE

Mabel Livingstone

Mana-Zucca

In well-marked rhythm

I think that the dog-wood was named for the dog;

The cat - nip was named for the cat;

I think that the cow-slip was named for the cow;

And that's all I know a-bout that,

Slower

And that's all I know a-bout · that.

The Whistling Boy

ROTE

Marjorie Knapp   German Folk Tune

1. I know a whis - tling boy; · ·
2. You can - not keep him still, · ·

No mat - ter what he has to do,
He whis - tles morn-ing, night and noon;

He whis - tles a - way at work or play
If ev - er you've heard a sing - ing bird,

And goes on whis-tling, whis-tling till he's through.
You know how gay and mer - ry is his tune.

(Whistle)
(Whistle)

Whistling Boy

Painted by the American artist FRANK DUVENECK,
and now in the Cincinnati Museum of Art

French Market Song

Carol Fuller

Carol Fuller

In jolly spirit

1. Hay, la, la; ho, la! Oh, Don-key and I,
2. Hay, la, la; ho, la! O Don-key, take care!
3. Hay, la, la; ho, la! If no one should buy,

Trot-ting to mar-ket with chees - es and pie,
If you should tum-ble, we'd nev - er get there,
We'll eat those chees-es, my Don - key and I;

Trot-ting to mar-ket with chees-es and pie.
If you should tum-ble, we'd nev - er get there.
We'll eat those chees-es, my Don-key and I.

Hay, la, la; ho, la! Oh, Don-key and I!
Hay, la, la; ho, la! O Don-key, take care!
Hay, la, la; ho, la! If no one should buy!

The Bee and the Baby

Louise Ayres Garnett

Austrian Folk Tune

1. Bum - ble, um - ble, boom, boom,
2. Bum - ble, um - ble, boom, boom,

Jum - ble, jum - ble, zoom, zoom!
Jum - ble, jum - ble, zoom, zoom!

Why do bees go buzz - ing round her
It's be - cause the ba - by's laugh - ter

As if they a - lone had found her?
Seems more sweet than what they're aft - er.

Bum - ble, um - ble, boom, boom.
Bum - ble, um - ble, boom, boom.

3

The Woodcutters

English version by
Louise Kessler

Finnish Folk Song

With strong accent

1. 'Neath the pine trees wood-men are sing-ing
2. Now a might-y pine tree is fall-ing,

As they send their sharp ax-es swing-ing.
Words of warn-ing wood-men are call-ing.

In the clear cold air sounds are ring-ing;
O'er the snow the logs they are haul-ing;

Brave-ly work the wood-men bold. ·
Brave-ly work the wood-men bold. ·

The Fruit Man

Susanna Myers

Transylvanian Folk Tune

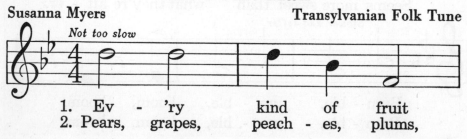

Not too slow

1. Ev - 'ry kind of fruit
2. Pears, grapes, peach - es, plums,

The Fruit Man (*Continued*)

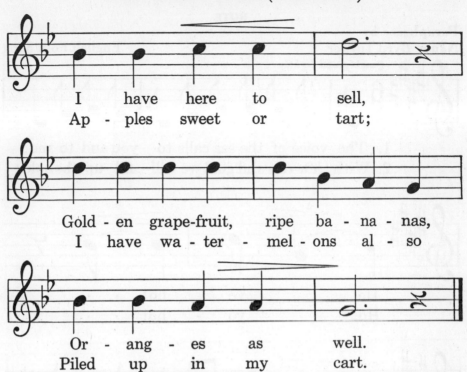

I have here to sell,
Ap - ples sweet or tart;

Gold - en grape-fruit, ripe ba - na - nas,
I have wa - ter - mel - ons al - so

Or - ang - es as well.
Piled up in my cart.

Call of the Sea

ROTE

Paraphrase by
Nancy Byrd Turner

English Folk Song

Quickly and lightly

1. The voice of the sea calls to you and to me;
2. With jew-els and gold we will fill up the hold;

Ho, . . yo - ho! . .
Ho, . . yo - ho! . .

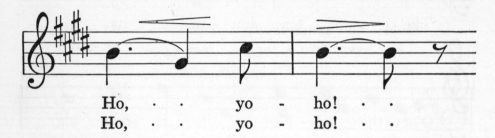

We'll sail far a - way · for man-y a day;
Then through the white foam we'll come sail-ing home

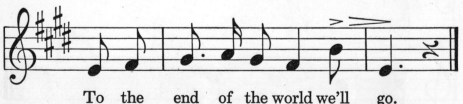

To the end of the world we'll go.
With a song and a loud "yo - ho!"

The Stream

Elizabeth Garrett

Polish Folk Tune

Un - der - neath a nar - row bridge
The wa - ter hur - ries by.
O'er the peb - bles it is flow - ing,
To the o - cean it is go - ing,
Far a - way.
Can you tell me why?

The Rabbit's Lunch

Marchette Gaylord Chute

Dutch Melody

Playfully

1. Once there was a lit - tle rab - bit
2. Though he had been ver - y care - ful,
3. But the rab - bit did - n't both - er;
4. So he shared his bas - ket with them,

Who went out to see the world,
Wear - ing noth - ing but his best,
He just o - pened up his lunch,
And they drank up all the tea;

With his din - ner in a bas - ket, And his
Not a sin - gle tur - tle e - ven Said how
And the tur - tles and the wood-chucks All came
And he showed them his um - brel - la Which they

whis-kers neat - ly curled; And he car-ried by its
fine - ly he was dressed; No one spoke a-bout his
run-ning in a bunch; For they might not like his
were most pleased to see; And they all went home to-

han - dle An um - brel - la which he whirled.
whis-kers, No one no-ticed his new vest.
waist-coat But they all en - joyed his lunch.
geth - er Just as hap-py as could be.

The Traveler

Anna Bird Stewart   Austrian Folk Tune

Happily, in well-marked rhythm

1. I should like to sail a - way
2. I should like to trav - el far

To vis - it for - eign lands;
And eat some for - eign meals;

I'd see so man - y new things,
Then home to tell my play - mates,

I'd trav - el round and do things;
My neigh-bors and my play - mates,

I'd play on for - eign sands.
Just how a trav - 'ler feels.

The Sailor

Marchette Gaylord Chute   ROTE   Jamaican Folk Tune

1. As I went walk-ing in Span-ish Town,
2. He had brought mon-keys a-cross the sea,
3. He said he knew of some hid-den gold

Up and down Span-ish Town,
I-vo-ry, crates of tea;
In an old se-cret hold;

I met a fine sail-or so big and brown,
And two lit-tle par-rots he gave to me
Oh, won-der-ful, won-der-ful tales he told

As I went up and down.
As we went up and down.
As we went up and down!

Mother's Hands

After the original by
Louise Ayres Garnett

Persian Folk Song

With feeling

1. When I see my moth - er's hands,
2. Some - times when I watch her hands

Man - y things to me they say;
They are like a flock of words,

Al - ways for oth - ers they are
Mak - ing a kind of verse as

work - ing ev - 'ry day. So I still re -
sweet as sing - ing birds. There is song in

mem - ber them, though I am far a - way.
Moth - er's hands. Her fin - gers seem like words.

The Night Air Mail

Catherine Parmenter   Norwegian Folk Tune

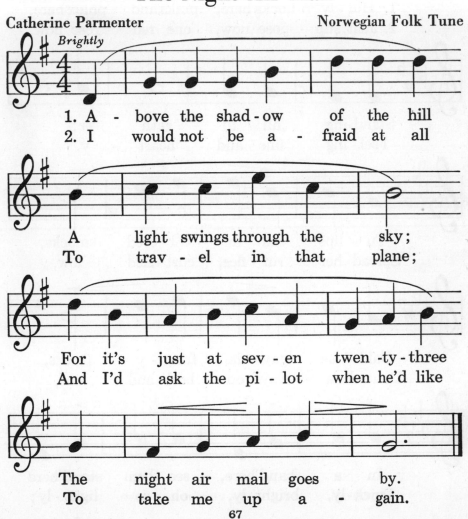

Brightly

1. A - bove the shad - ow   of   the   hill
2. I   would not   be   a - fraid   at   all

A   light swings through the   sky;
To   trav - el   in   that   plane;

For it's   just   at sev - en   twen -ty - three
And I'd   ask   the pi - lot   when he'd like

The   night   air   mail goes   by.
To   take   me   up   a -   gain.

67

A Garden Party

Nancy Byrd Turner

Polish Folk Tune

1. Hol - ly - hocks here, pinks and phlox here,
2. Just sup - pose now, one red rose now,

Stand-ing all to - geth - er;
Feel - ing fine and heart - y,

Tu - lips tall in col - ored smocks,
Spread her ruf - fles, curt - sied low,

Dahl - ias gay in fring - y frocks,
Danced a - way on heel and toe,

In a band here, see them stand here
Quick-ly, bright-ly, oh, so light - ly;

Through the sum - mer weath - er.
What a gar - den par - ty!

Your Home and Mine

Nancy Byrd Turner   Austrian Folk Tune

With tenderness

1. You love your home be - cause it is yours,
2. I love my home be - cause it is mine,

Win-dows and hall and porch and doors;
Co - sy and warm, with lights that shine;

Eaves where swal - lows make them a nest;
Rooms for play - ing, rooms where we rest;

Homes are for love, and you love yours best.
Homes are for love, and I love mine best.

The Rainbow

Mary C. Gleitz

Danish Folk Tune

With expression

1. Look at the rain - bow bright!
2. What if I should be blown

It is like a bridge of light;
To the rain - bow all a - lone?

Red, or - ange, blue and green,
I would not be a - fraid,

Bright - est col - ors ev - er seen,
I could see how rain is made

'Way up so high.
High in the sky.

Jolly Little Eskimo

ROTE

E. H. Tewksbury

R. T. Bjorkman

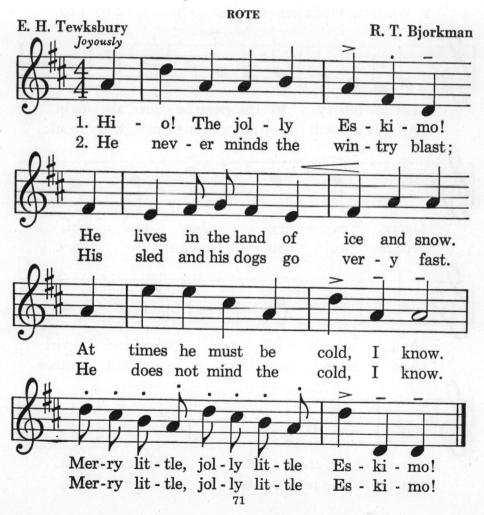

Joyously

1. Hi - o! The jol - ly Es - ki - mo!
2. He nev - er minds the win - try blast;

He lives in the land of ice and snow.
His sled and his dogs go ver - y fast.

At times he must be cold, I know.
He does not mind the cold, I know.

Mer - ry lit - tle, jol - ly lit - tle Es - ki - mo!
Mer - ry lit - tle, jol - ly lit - tle Es - ki - mo!

71

Dancing on the Green

Louise Ayres Garnett

Polish Folk Tune

1. We have had our sup-per and it still is light;
2. When the clock has struck and I have gone to bed,

Let us hur-ry to the green be-fore 'tis night.
All our fun will keep on run-ning through my head:

Dance, ev-'ry boy and girl,
Dreams will com-mence to dance,

And prance with a twist and twirl
And beams from the moon will prance

And watch the stars grow-ing bright.
And whis-per words nev-er said.

Making Flour

Kate Forman   Hungarian Folk Tune

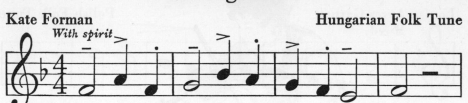

1. Hay, mill-er! Ho, mill-er! Here is our wheat!
2. Hay, lad-die! Ho, lad-die! Here is your flour!

Come, take it; please make it read-y to eat.
I've weighed it, I've made it all in one hour;

How the wind blows! How the grain flows!
Round the mill flew when the wind blew.

Rap, tap-ping, clap, clap-ping, so the mill goes.
Come, take it, now bake it! This is for you.

My Fiddle

J. Katherine Mixter

Arthur Targett

With simplicity

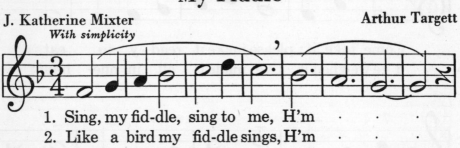

1. Sing, my fid-dle, sing to me, H'm · · ·
2. Like a bird my fid-dle sings, H'm · · ·

Sing a song of mirth and glee! H'm · · ·

Sweet and soft its mu - sic rings, H'm · · ·

Sing, my fid-dle, to the bow, H'm · ·

Lis - ten while I soft-ly play: H'm · ·

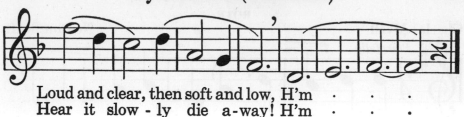

Loud and clear, then soft and low, H'm . . .
Hear it slow - ly die a-way! H'm . . .

Flowers and Birds

Mary Smith   Wolfgang Amadeus Mozart

Gracefully

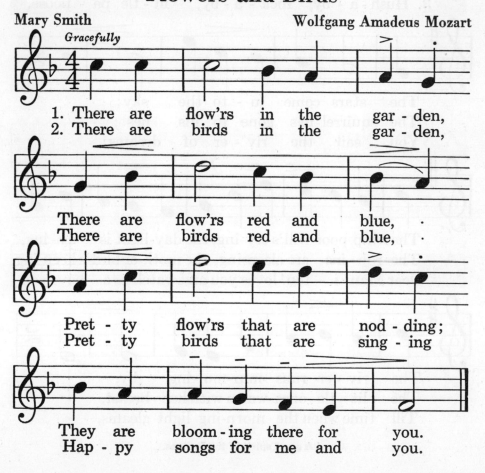

1. There are flow'rs in the gar - den,
2. There are birds in the gar - den,

There are flow'rs red and blue, .
There are birds red and blue, .

Pret - ty flow'rs that are nod - ding;
Pret - ty birds that are sing - ing

They are bloom - ing there for you.
Hap - py songs for me and you.

Indian Lullaby

ROTE

Charles Myall

Newton Swift

Peacefully

1. Rock - a - by, hush - a - by, lit - tle pa - poose,
2. Pine trees are slum - ber - ing, lit - tle pa - poose,
3. Hush - a - by, rock - a - by, lit - tle pa - poose,

The stars come in - to the sky; · ·
The squirrel has gone to his nest; · ·
You sail the riv - er of dreams; · ·

The whip-poor-will's cry-ing, the day-light is dy-ing,
The rob - ins are sleep-ing, the moth-er bird's keep-ing
Dear Man - i - tou[1] loves you and watch-es a - bove you

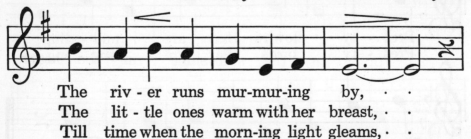

The riv - er runs mur-mur-ing by, · ·
The lit - tle ones warm with her breast, · ·
Till time when the morn-ing light gleams, · ·

[1] A great spirit of the Indians.

Mur-mur-ing by, · ·   mur-mur-ing by. · ·
Warm with her breast, ·   warm with her breast. ·
Morn-ing light gleams, ·   morn-ing light gleams. ·

Sunshine

Anonymous   Mary Root Kern

Work a lit - tle, play a lit - tle,

Don't for - get to sing;

For 'tis the sun - shine in the heart

That bright - ens ev - 'ry - thing.

Cling Clang

M. A. L. Lane

Czechoslovakian Folk Tune

With strong accent

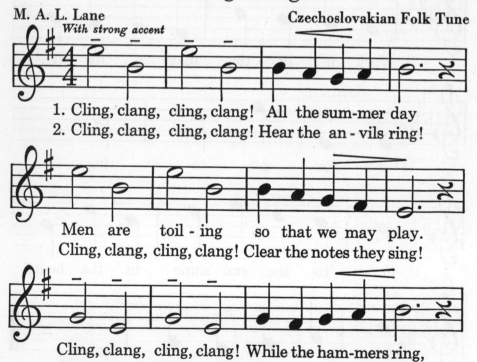

1. Cling, clang, cling, clang! All the sum-mer day
2. Cling, clang, cling, clang! Hear the an - vils ring!

Men are toil - ing so that we may play.
Cling, clang, cling, clang! Clear the notes they sing!

Cling, clang, cling, clang! While the ham-mers ring,
Cling, clang, cling, clang! Dust - y is the air;

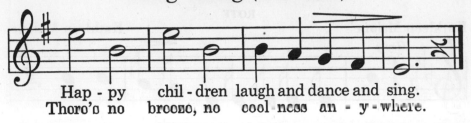

Hap - py   chil - dren laugh and dance and sing.
Thoro'o no   brooms, no   cool nooo an - y - where.

The Oriole

Carol Fuller

Jean Baptiste de Lully
Air from "Le Bourgeois Gentilhomme"

With expression

1. O - ri - ole   gold - en, what do you   say,
2. O - ri - ole   gold - en, where is your   nest?

Sing - ing and   wing - ing a - cross my   way?
Which lit - tle   bird do you   love the   best?

Are you not   wea - ry,   sing - ing so   long?
Have you some   chil - dren   up in the   tree?

O - ri - ole,   o - ri - ole, lend me your   song!
O - ri - ole,   o - ri - ole, show them to   me.

The Christmas Tree

ROTE

Kathleen Malone   Kathleen Malone

How   love - ly are the trees in   the spring-time,

In   the sum-mer-time · and in   the   fall!

But   the   Christ-mas tree   is   fair   to   see,

And   the   love - li - est   tree   of   all!

The First Christmas

81

After the original by
Ethel Crowninshield

French Carol

Gracefully

1. From o-ver the hill ver-y far, far a-way
2. How qui-et the sta-ble, how sweet was the hay!

Came wise men and shep-herds that first Christ-mas day;
How lov-ing the moth-er who watched where He lay!

The star in the sky, they had fol-lowed its light
For shep-herds and wise men how bless-ed the sight!

To where in a man-ger, quite plain to their sight,
How rich were the gifts, and how ten-der the light

The dear Christ-mas Ba-by was sleep-ing that night.
That shone in the eyes of the watch-ers that night!

Merry Christmas

Traditional   Traditional

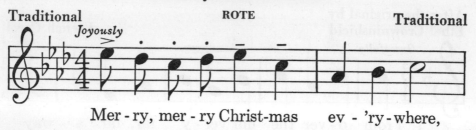

Mer - ry, mer - ry Christ-mas   ev - 'ry - where,

Cheer - i - ly   it ring - eth   through the   air,

Christ-mas bells, Christ-mas trees, Christ-mas car - ols

on the breeze. Mer-ry, mer-ry Christ-mas ev-'ry-where,

Cheer - i - ly   it ring - eth   through the   air.

Merry Christmas (*Continued*)

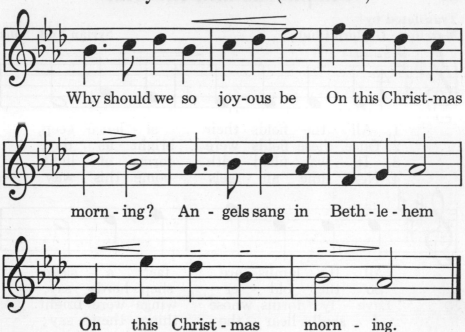

Why should we so joy-ous be On this Christ-mas

morn - ing? An - gels sang in Beth - le - hem

On this Christ - mas morn - ing.

84   **Shepherds and the Star**

Translated by
Marchette Gaylord Chute

Syrian Folk Song

1. All the fields their si-lence keep,
2. Once these fields were bright as day,
3. It was filled with forms of light,
4. Next time an-gels come this way

All the lambs are fast a-sleep;
So the old-er shep-herds say,
Love-ly forms, whose wings were bright.
I shall hear the things they say;

I a-lone must keep a-wake, Watch-ing for their sake;
When a-cross the mid-night sky One white star went by;
What the shep-herds heard them say They have hid a-way;
For a-lone out here I lie, Look-ing at the sky;

Low and qui-et songs I make, As I keep a-wake.
All the shep-herds gave a cry As they watched the sky.
I can nev-er make them say What they heard that day.
We shall see that star go by, Lit-tle lambs and I.

Cousin Michael

ROTE

Translation by
Cecil Cowdrey

German Folk Song

Merrily

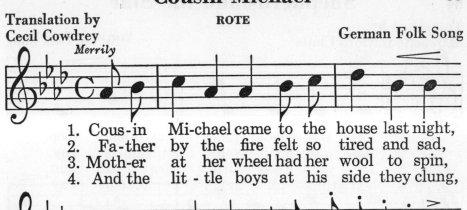

1. Cous-in   Mi-chael came to the   house last night,
2. Fa-ther   by the   fire felt so   tired and sad,
3. Moth-er   at her wheel had her   wool to spin,
4. And the   lit-tle boys at his   side they clung,

As we   all sat round by the yel-low can-dle-light;
Cous-in   Mi-chael came and it made him ver-y glad;
Cous-in Mi-chael knocked and we asked him to come in;
On his   ev-'ry look with de-light and joy they hung;

As we   all sat there by the can-dle-light,
Cous-in   Mi-chael laughed, cous-in Mi-chael sang,
What with this   to   say, what with that to tell,
Of his horse, his dog, they could miss no word;

Cous-in   Mi-chael came to our house last night.
And he shook his purse and the   pen-nies rang.
Cous-in   Mi-chael pleased moth-er ver-y well.
Sto-ries such as these they had nev-er heard.

Christmas Carol

ROTE

Ethel Crowninshield

Austrian Folk Tune

Gracefully

1. Bright star of Christ - mas,
2. Low in a man - ger

The shep-herds have seen you to-night; Bright star of
The Beth-le-hem Babe they have found; Though they be

Christ-mas The wise men will fol - low your light.
stran-gers, He smiles at them kneel-ing a - round.

O - ver the sta-ble, Where sheep and cat-tle stay,
Gifts they will bring Him, Then up and on their way,

Star, bright-ly shin-ing, You bring the Christ-mas day.
Filled with the won-der Of that first Christ-mas day.

Last Night

Helena D. Koletzke

C. D. Daniel

Quietly

1. Last night the trees were cold and bare
2. I won-der which they like the best,

And shiv - ered so!
What win - ter weaves,

But now a fluff - y coat they wear
Or branch-es bare, or to be dressed

Of shin - ing snow.
In cool, green leaves.

Gifts

Elizabeth Garrett

Tyrolean Carol

Gifts I have not of sil - ver or jew - els,

But songs I'll sing of that first Christ - mas day;

Thoughts of love and of joy I am bring - ing

To the Ba - by a - sleep on the hay;

Gifts I have not of sil - ver or jew - els,

But lov - ing thoughts go to Him on this day.

With Our Sleds

Louise Kessler

Finnish Folk Tune

1. Down the hill - side we are slid - ing,
2. "Clear the way," the boys are call - ing,

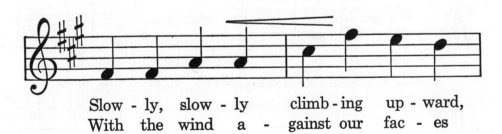

Smooth   is   the   snow:
Hark   to   the   cry!

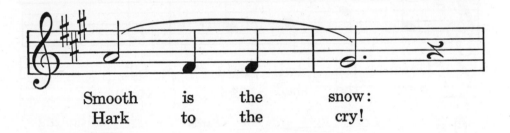

Slow - ly, slow - ly climb - ing up - ward,
With the wind a - gainst our fac - es

Down   a - gain   we   go.
We   are   fly - ing   by.

3

Chinese Evening Song

Nancy Byrd Turner

Chinese Folk Tune[1]

With expression

1. Tem - ple bells ring   soft and clear
2. Birds are drow - sy   in their nest,

Down   the   twi - light   hill,
Slow   the   shad - ows   creep,

Dusk-y qui-et hill   Where the shad-ows fill.
Tip-toe shad-ows creep,   Dark is grow-ing deep.

Softer

Ling   Foo,   go   to   sleep, my   dear,
All   the   world has   gone   to   rest,

[1] From the "Botsford Collection of Folk-Songs," compiled and edited by Florence Hudson Botsford, Volume One. Copyright 1922 and 1930 by G. Schirmer, Inc. Printed by permission.

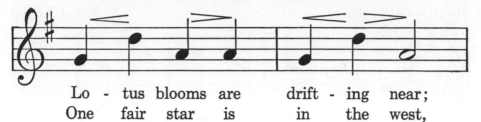

Lo - tus blooms are drift - ing near;
One fair star is in the west,

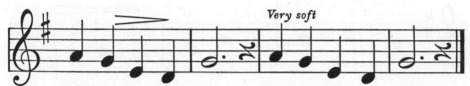

Very soft

Night is on the hill; Tem-ple bells are still.
And a watch will keep. Ling Foo, go to sleep.

There Was a Goose

Mabel Livingstone   Victor Young

There was a goose from Goos - ey - ville

Who stood be - side · a grass - y hill;

She would - n't budge, she would - n't stir,

She said the hill · should come to her.

But this the hill · re - fused to do

Be - cause the hill was stub-born too.

Stars

Ruth McConn Spencer   Ruth McConn Spencer

Peacefully

When I go to bed at night Stars are shin-ing

ver - y bright; When I wake at morn next day

The pret-ty stars have gone a - way. Moth-er says the

stars are there, But I can't see them an - y-where.

Skating

Ethel Crowninshield   German Folk Tune

1. Win - ter is near, days cold and clear!
2. Light - ly we glide here side by side,

Out of the north the wind may blow.
While o - ver - head the sky is blue.

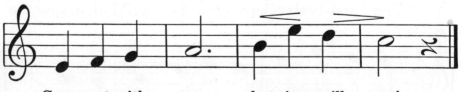

It is for skat - ing we have been wait - ing.
Like a bird fly - ing, speed with-out try - ing,

Come out with me, skat - ing we'll go!
O - ver the ice, skat - ing with you!

Game of Flowers

ROTE

After the original by
Beatrice Wadhams

French Folk Song

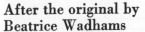

Mau-rice shall be a pop-py, Ma-rie shall be a rose;

This is a game of flow-ers, A-round and round it goes!

Now you shall be a dai-sy And I a vi'-let blue.

Come, dance in the rose ring, All take hands a-round Ma-rie!

Come, dance in the rose ring! Till she calls for you.

Echo

Thomas Grant Springer

Victor Young

Merrily

1. There's some-one lives up - on the hill,
2. I guess he is - n't ver - y bright,

Though fa-ther says, "Oh, no!" But when down here it's
He mocks me here be-low; For when I shout with

all so still, If I sing here be -
all my might, "I wish that you would

low, "Hel - lo, hel - lo, hel - lo, hel - lo";
go; Good - by, good - by, good - by, good - by";

Softly

"Hel - lo, hel - lo, hel - lo, hel - lo," The
"Good - by, good - by, good - by, good - by," He

oth-er fel-low an-swers, so That's how I know.
an-swers back, but does-n't go. He teas-es so.

Winter

Mary Smith

Slovak Folk Tune

Not too slow

1. Cold win - ter days are here,
2. Ap - ples are roast - ing there,

Dark - est of all the year;
Pol - ished with great - est care;

Close by the fire we hear
Pop - corn with flow'rs of white,

Sto-ries of fun and cheer, Songs of ad - ven-ture.
Ros - y the glow-ing light; Joys of the win - ter.

The Miller of Arden

ROTE

After the original by
Nancy Byrd Turner

English Folk Song

Merrily

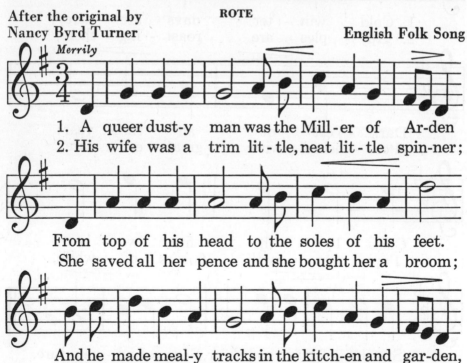

1. A queer dust-y man was the Mill-er of Ar-den
2. His wife was a trim lit-tle, neat lit-tle spin-ner;

From top of his head to the soles of his feet.
She saved all her pence and she bought her a broom;

And he made meal-y tracks in the kitch-en and gar-den,
So that when he came home ev-'ry day for his din-ner,

98

And left   a white trail on the   road and the   street.
She chased and she dust-ed him   all round the room.

Wooden Shoe Dance

Marchette Gaylord Chute   Swedish Folk Tune

In well-marked rhythm

1. "Choose your part-ners!   Ev-'ry-bod-y choose!"
2. "Whirl your part-ners!   Whirl them all a-round!"

Hil - da's   danc - ing   feet   go
O - laf   turns   to   Chris - tine;

Tap, tap, tap   in   lit - tle wood-en shoes,
Wood-en shoes hop   gay - ly o'er the ground,

While   to   Nels   she   curt - sies   low.
While they dance   up - on   the   green.

Wonderings

Aileen Fisher   Italian Folk Tune

1. I won-der if a flow-er knows
2. I won-der if there's an - y way

If it is a dan - de - lion or rose;
For straw to find out it is - n't hay;

Or if a flock of birds can say,
And does a worm, do you sup - pose,

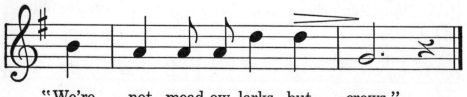

"We're not mead-ow larks, but crows."
Wish it were a bug with toes?

Song of the Violin

Mary Smith

Danish Folk Tune

Joyfully

1. If I could play the vi - o - lin,
2. I'd play a - bout the fair - y folk

I would make a mer - ry, mer - ry tune;
Danc - ing in their dain - ty lit - tle shoon,[1]

I'd play a - bout the fair - ies
A - danc - ing on the sil - ver

That dance up - on the moon.
That paves the shin - ing moon.

[1] An old English word for " shoes."

Pancakes

Elizabeth Garrett

Czech Folk Tune

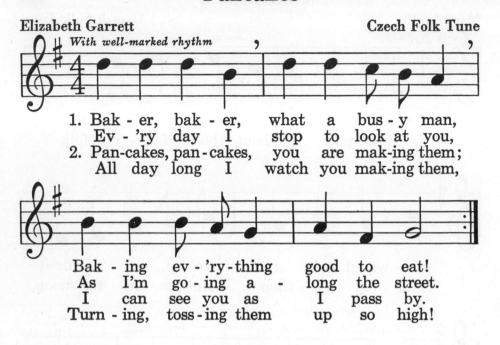

With well-marked rhythm

1. Bak - er, bak - er, what a bus - y man,
   Ev - 'ry day I stop to look at you,
2. Pan-cakes, pan-cakes, you are mak-ing them;
   All day long I watch you mak-ing them,

Bak - ing ev - 'ry-thing good to eat!
As I'm go - ing a - long the street.
I can see you as I pass by.
Turn - ing, toss-ing them up so high!

Books

Marjorie Knapp

Ukrainian Folk Tune

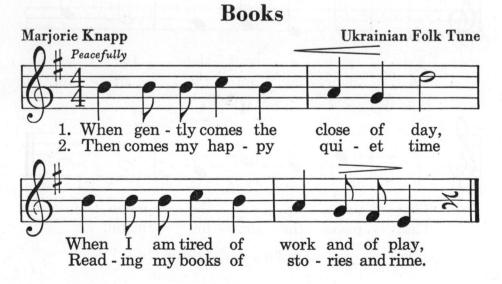

Peacefully

1. When gen - tly comes the close of day,
2. Then comes my hap - py qui - et time

When I am tired of work and of play,
Read - ing my books of sto - ries and rime.

Rabbit and the Hunter

**Translated by
Cecil Cowdrey**

Slavic Folk Song

1. Bun-ny, bun-ny, sit-ting by the mead-ow way,
2. Bun-ny, bun-ny, when you hear the hunt-er's horn,
3. Bun-ny, do not stop to breathe nor say "good-day,"
4. Bun-ny, bun-ny, you have done the best you could!

Do you hear the hunt-er's horn this sum-mer day?
Up and off and skip in-to the field of corn!
Do not stop to ask your friend the short-est way!
Here with-in the deep, green for-est, rest is good!

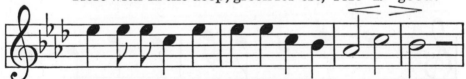

Soon, ver-y soon, the hunt-er and his hounds will pass,
Run, run a-long through fields of clo-ver, hop, hop, hop!
On through the fur-rows, past the bars, so swift-ly go!
Gone is the hunt-er; hear his horn so far a-way!

Soon, ver-y soon, they'll spy lit-tle bun-ny in the grass!
Run, lit-tle bun-ny, run, lit-tle bun-ny, do not stop!
On-ly the wind and on-ly the bend-ing grass will know!
Dear lit-tle bun-ny, now you are safe while here you stay.

Growing

Hope Ann Rhodes

Yugoslavian Folk Tune

1. Once the trees were ver - y small,
2. Some grow fast and some grow slow,

Trees that now are ver - y, ver - y tall;
But like me, they nev - er, nev - er know;

That's what hap - pens to one and all;
On - ly aft - er a while we show

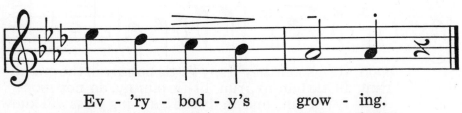

Ev - 'ry - bod - y's grow - ing.
How we all are grow - ing.

Washington and Lincoln

ROTE

Ethel Crowninshield

Belgian Folk Tune

With spirit

1. Wash - ing - ton, our brav - est one!
2. Sing a song of Lin - coln too!

Sing of deeds that he has done!
Lin - coln, ev - er brave and true!

Though he lived so long a - go,
Stars and stripes that wave on high

Ev - 'ry child his name should know.
We'll sa - lute as we pass by.

3

Feeding Her Birds

Painted by the French artist JEAN FRANÇOIS MILLET,
in 1860. It is now in the Lille Museum, France

Feeding Her Birds

Luther Wilde

Czech Folk Tune

Smoothly and gracefully

1. Three lit - tle birds of mine,
2. Perched in the cot - tage door,

Six mer - ry eyes that shine; O - pen, my
Each in her pin - a - fore, Rest, lit - tle

spar-rows, your hun - gry mouths, And you shall
birds, in my ten - der love, Then spread your

sup and dine. O - pen, my spar-rows, your
wings and soar. Rest, lit - tle birds, in my

hun - gry mouths, And you shall sup and dine.
ten - der love, Then spread your wings and soar.

Pony's Birthday

After the original by
Nellie Poorman

Finnish Folk Song

1. Black-smith, black-smith, I've a gift to choose;
2. Har - ness mak - er,   will you wait on me?

Make two pairs of   lit - tle i - ron shoes!
Pret - ty   har - ness   I should like to see;

Shape them quick - ly,   there's no time to lose:
Red   and   shin - y   must the leath-er be:

To - day is po - ny's   birth - day.
To - day is po - ny's   birth - day.

Dancing in the Woods

ROTE

Frederick H. Martens

Bohemian-Czech Folk Tune

1. Deep in the for - est the shad-ows are play-ing,
2. O - ver the peb-bles the lit - tle stream danc-es,

And we're play-ing with them, sing tra-la-la-la-la-la!
And we'll dance be-side it, sing tra-la - la-la-la - la!

High o - ver - head sum-mer breez - es are sing-ing,
Down in the mead-ows a bright gold-en car - pet

And we're sing-ing with them, sing tra-la-la-la-la-la!
Is spread for our danc-ing, sing tra-la-la-la-la - la!

Sun in the Sky

Louise Ayres Garnett   Louise Ayres Garnett

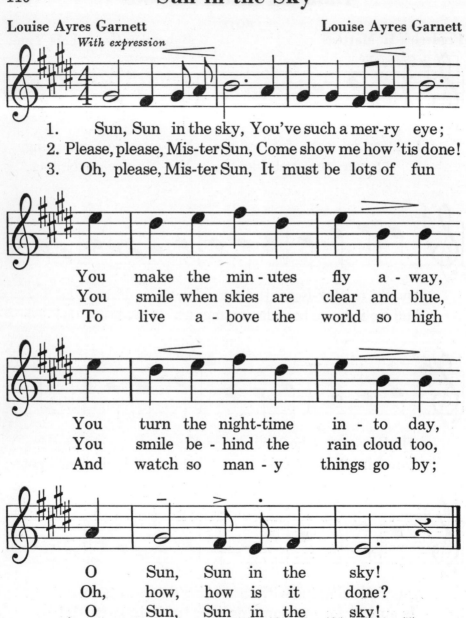

1.   Sun, Sun in the sky, You've such a mer-ry   eye;
2. Please, please, Mis-ter Sun, Come show me how 'tis done!
3.   Oh, please, Mis-ter Sun, It must be lots of   fun

You   make the min - utes   fly   a - way,
You   smile when skies are   clear and blue,
To   live   a - bove the   world so   high

You   turn the night-time   in - to   day,
You   smile be - hind the   rain cloud too,
And   watch so   man - y   things go   by;

O   Sun,   Sun in   the   sky!
Oh,   how,   how is   it   done?
O   Sun,   Sun in   the   sky!

Hop Sing Lee

Lily Strickland   **Lily Strickland**

1. In a lit - tle town far   o'er the   sea
2. When he sends his lit - tle   kite so   high

Lives a   lit - tle boy named   Hop   Sing   Lee,
Like a   bird a - fly - ing   in   the   sky,

With his   lit - tle bowls of   rice   and   tea,
Lit - tle   Hop Sing danc - es   in   his   glee;

Eat - ing with his chop-sticks,   Hop Sing Lee.
Likes to   eat   and play, does   Hop Sing Lee.

Midsummer's Night

After the original by
Louise Kessler

Estonian Folk Song

With well-marked rhythm

1. In the woods there is a mag - ic fern,
2. Seek the mag - ic flow-er 'neath the moon,

Mag - ic fern, mag - ic fern,
'Neath the moon, 'neath the moon,

In the woods there is a mag - ic fern,
Seek the mag - ic flow-er 'neath the moon,

Bloom - ing on Mid - sum - mer's Night.
Long - est day in all the year.

Midsummer's Night *(Continued)*

113

Come, come, fol-low me, Danc-ing through the woods with glee!
Come, come, dance and sing! In the woods our voic-es ring.

Come, come, fol-low me! Soon the mag-ic fern we'll see.
Come, come, dance and sing! Joy to me the fern will bring.

Merry-go-round

ROTE

Mabel Livingstone

Victor Young

Mer - ry - go - round, go round, go round,

Mer-ry-go-round, go round. John-ny shall ride a

pranc - ing horse And Jack a hunt - ing

hound. · Ted-dy shall drive a gild - ed coach,

Bil - ly can sit in - side; · Mer-ry-go-round, go

round, go round, Give us a jol - ly ride! ·

The Shower

M. Louise Baum

Cornelius Gurlitt

1. Pit-ter pat-ter falls the mer - ry rain,
2. Pit-ter pat-ter, still the rain-drops run,

Pit-ter pat -ter calls at ev - 'ry pane,
Pit-ter pat - ter, till their work is done;

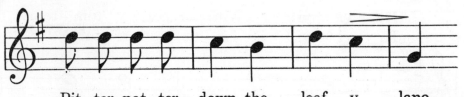

Pit - ter pat - ter down the leaf - y lane,
Scam-per now, for see, there comes the sun

So light - ly the rain is danc - ing.
With man - y a sun-beam glanc - ing.

Indians

Louise Kessler   Robert W. Gibb

1. Hi yi yi! We are lit-tle In-dians
2. Hi yi yi! Lit-tle broth-er rab-bit

Danc-ing here, danc-ing here.
Runs a-way, runs a-way;

Hi yi yi! With our nois-y tom-toms
Hi yi yi! Lit-tle broth-er rab-bit

Loud and clear, loud and clear.
Will not play, will not play.

In-dian boys in a cir-cle danc-ing,
In-dian boys in the mead-ow scuff-ling,

Indians (*Continued*)

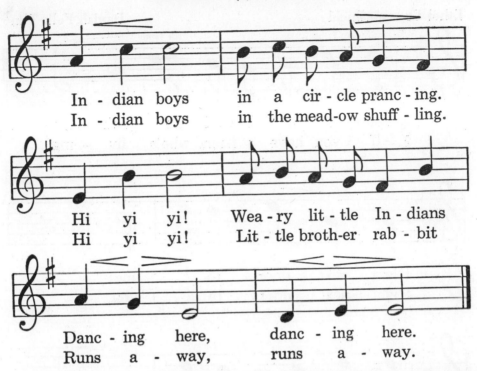

In - dian boys   in a cir - cle pranc - ing.
In - dian boys   in the mead-ow shuff - ling.

Hi yi yi!   Wea - ry lit - tle In - dians
Hi yi yi!   Lit - tle broth-er rab - bit

Danc - ing here,   danc - ing here.
Runs a - way,   runs a - way.

Neighbors

Ethel Crowninshield

Danish Folk Tune

In moderate time

1. Soon a call I shall be mak - ing
2. If you have a friend who's liv - ing

Right next door to me;
Right next door to you,

To my neigh-bor I'll be tak - ing
You can have the fun of giv - ing

Some-thing he will like to see.
Some-thing to your neigh -bor too.

The Airplane

Annette Wynne

Czechoslovakian Folk Tune

With spirit

1. The air-plane flies ver - y fast and high;
2. The air-plane goes ver - y fast and high;

Fly, plane, fly!
Fly, plane, fly!

Oh, the air - plane flies in - to a cloud
As I watch it from the street be - low,

While the en - gine sings a song quite loud:
Like a bird the plane through clouds can go:

Fly, plane, fly! The plane like a bird goes by.
Fly, plane, fly! The air pi-lot loves the sky.

Oopsy Daisy Oh!

ROTE

Louise Ayres Garnett

Yugoslavian Folk Tune

Lightly, with swaying rhythm

1. Go-ing up in a swing is a jol - ly thing;
2. Go-ing up makes a breeze in the tops of trees;

Oop-sy dai - sy oh! oop-sy dai - sy oh!
Oop-sy dai - sy oh! oop-sy dai - sy oh!

Com-ing down with a swoop near-ly loops a loop;
Com-ing down all the ground seems to turn a - round;

Oh, oop - sy dai - dai - sy, oop-sy dai - sy!
Oh, oop - sy dai - dai - sy, oop-sy dai - sy!

No - bod-y's la - zy, dai-sy oh! .
Ev - 'ry-thing's ha - zy, dai-sy oh! .

The Candle

Marchette Gaylord Chute

Russian Folk Tune

1. It is night, and the streets are cold;
2. All the stars are a - way to - night;

Snow has filled the air.
On - ly one wee spark

See, the win - ter wind has rolled
From a can - dle's yel - low light

Snow - drifts ev - 'ry - where.
Shines out through the dark.

Prayer

Johann Sebastian Bach
From the "Christmas Oratorio"

Elizabeth Garrett

1. God   cares for ev - 'ry - one   in His sight;
2. This   day I've ev - er been   in His care,

He   watch-es   o - ver us both day and night.
This   night I kneel to Him and make my prayer:

What - e'er we   do or where - ev - er we   go,
My   thanks I'll give to Him, then I shall rest;

God guides our thoughts that the right we may know.
A   grate-ful heart is the prayer He likes best.

Infant Samuel Praying

Painted by the English artist SIR JOSHUA REYNOLDS.
It is now in the National Gallery, London, England

A Golden Boat I'll Buy You

**English version by
Carol Fuller**

Swedish Folk Song

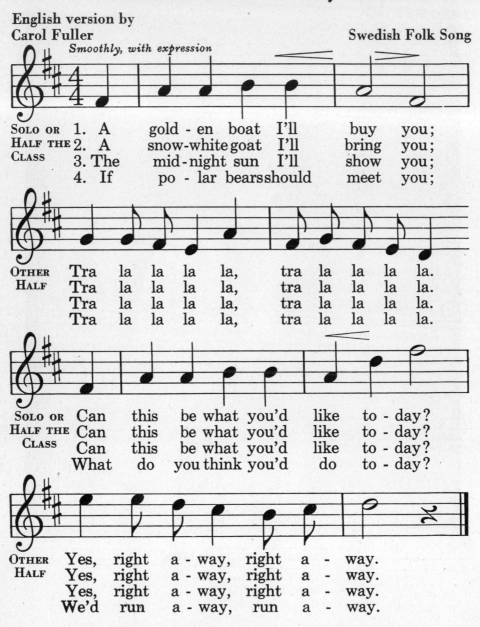

Smoothly, with expression

SOLO OR
HALF THE
CLASS

1. A gold - en boat I'll buy you;
2. A snow-white goat I'll bring you;
3. The mid-night sun I'll show you;
4. If po - lar bears should meet you;

OTHER
HALF

Tra la la la la, tra la la la la.
Tra la la la la, tra la la la la.
Tra la la la la, tra la la la la.
Tra la la la la, tra la la la la.

SOLO OR
HALF THE
CLASS

Can this be what you'd like to - day?
Can this be what you'd like to - day?
Can this be what you'd like to - day?
What do you think you'd do to - day?

OTHER
HALF

Yes, right a - way, right a - way.
Yes, right a - way, right a - way.
Yes, right a - way, right a - way.
We'd run a - way, run a - way.

Puddings and Pies

Josephine Royle

Alsatian Folk Tune

Playfully

1. When Ma - ry makes a pud - ding,
2. When Ma - ry makes some pas - try,

When Ma - ry bakes a pie,
When Ma - ry bakes a tart,

I stand be - side the kitch - en door
I go up - on my bend - ed knees

And this is what I cry, "Yum - yum!
And say with all my heart, "Yum - yum!

I want a piece of pie."
Oh, may I have a tart?"

3

In Holland

Mollie Gladstone

With spirit

Mollie Gladstone

Sea, O Sea! we know you're strong,

But our dikes will hold you long.

"Sea, O Sea, keep a - way from me!"

Said the mill - er by the Zuid - er Zee.

Winter Dream

Hope Ann Rhodes

With expression

Welsh Folk Tune

1. Buds and flow'rs will sleep Through the snow-y win-ter days,
2. Deep with-in their dream They will hear a blue-bird sing;

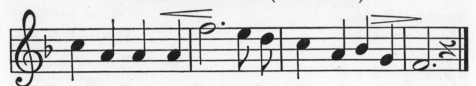

But their hearts will keep Hap-py thoughts of sum-mer ways.
Short the time will seem Till the com - ing of the spring.

Underneath the Willow

Marchette Gaylord Chute   French Folk Tune

Quietly

1. Un - der - neath the   wil - low,
2. Lit - tle birds come   near   me,

Clo - ver for my   pil - low,
Lit - tle frogs don't   fear   me,

This is the place where I like to   lie
All birds that nest in the wil - low   tree

Look-ing at the sky,   Just my-self and   I.
Sing a song to me,   To my-self and   me.

Peter and the Swan

English version by
Ethel Crowninshield

Russian Folk Song

Slowly and sweetly

1. Now the cold, cold winds are · blow - ing,
2. On the wa - ter she is · glid - ing,

Pe - ter to the lake is · go - ing;
From the wind she is not · hid - ing;

Win - ter's come and there's no know - ing
Slow and state - ly she is rid - ing

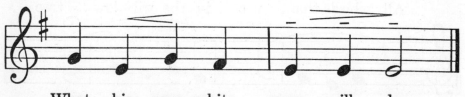

What his pure white swan will do.
In her feath - er coat so new.

Up and Down the Hill

ROTE

Louise Ayres Garnett

Melba Knaus Loughlin

With expression

1. Up on the hill where the sky is the near-est,
2. Down the same hill is a queer lit-tle hol-low

Sun-light and moon-light and star-light are clear-est;
Where I can hide me and no one will fol-low;

When I keep look-ing, the sky seems to lift me
Though I grow old-er than Fa-ther De-cem-ber,

High with the birds where the winds gen-tly drift me.
Hill-top and hol-low I'll al-ways re-mem-ber.

Old Glory

Nancy Byrd Turner

Austrian Folk Tune

With spirit

1. The flag, see it come, With fife and with drum!
2. Sa - lute it with song! It's mov-ing a - long.

For the light is fair in its folds and bars,
We will all keep read - y with heart and hand;

And the wind is free in its shin - ing stars;
We will do our part for our na - tive land;

And bright and brave and strong It moves a - long.
Old Glo - ry, bright on high, Goes march-ing by!

Come to the Garden

Mary Smith

Yugoslavian Folk Tune

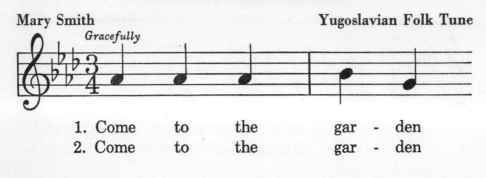

1. Come   to   the   gar - den
2. Come   to   the   gar - den

And   see   how   the   flow - ers   grow!
And   see   how   the   flow - ers   grow!

The seeds will be left in the earth aft-er rak-ing,
The seeds will a-wake and green dress-es be wear-ing.

Till sun-shine and rain will call, "Come now, be wak-ing."
Then soon each wee stem will a   blos-som be bear-ing.

Playing in the Sun

Louise Ayres Garnett

French Folk Tune

1. Take my hand, let us hur-ry out, Out in the sun.
2. We're read-y for an-oth-er game; Tag! You are "It."

First   we'll   go   whirl - ing   in   a   spin,
You   chase   a -   round the   ma - ple   tree,

Like   tops   when   spin - ning they   be - gin;
Cir - cle   the   mead - ow   aft - er   me!

Then we'll go run-ning all a-bout; Fun, oh, what fun!
Then we will find a shad-y spot Where we can sit.

Lady Spring

Cecil Cowdrey

Norwegian Folk Tune

Softly and smoothly

1. O - ver the hill, down by the mill,
2. Blos-som - ing trees sway in the breeze,

La - dy Spring comes sing - ing;
Birds her foot - steps fol - low;

Where the brook flows, laugh-ing she goes,
"Come out and see," Spring calls to me;

Light - ly her flow - ers fling - ing.
"Hur - ry," cry thrush and swal - low,

Sing - ing, comes La - dy Spring! · ·
"Wel-come her, La - dy Spring." · ·

The Dancing Wind

Carol Fuller   ROTE   Melba Knaus Loughlin

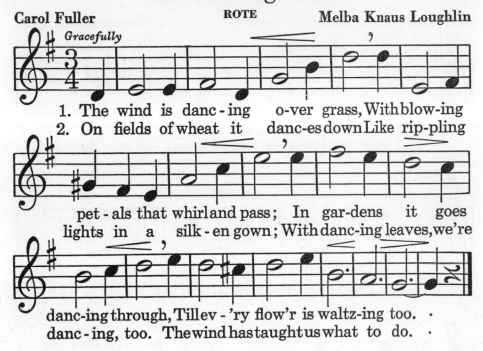

Gracefully

1. The wind is danc-ing o-ver grass, With blow-ing
2. On fields of wheat it danc-es down Like rip-pling

pet-als that whirl and pass; In gar-dens it goes
lights in a silk-en gown; With danc-ing leaves, we're

danc-ing through, Till ev-'ry flow'r is waltz-ing too. ·
danc-ing, too. The wind has taught us what to do. ·

The Deer

Elizabeth Garrett   Russian Folk Tune

Quietly

1. From the for-est, where the snow is ver-y deep,
2. When the snow has cov-ered up your win-ter store,

Come, lit-tle deer, I've food here for you to eat.
Come, lit-tle deer, And I'll al-ways give you more.

Down the Stream[1]

Derrick Norman Lehmer Collection   **Miwok Indian Song**

Steadily

1. Down the stream, down the stream, All the leaves go;
2. Down the stream, down the stream, All my days go;

Down the stream, down the stream, All the leaves go.
Down the stream, down the stream, All my days go.

Who can say, who can know, Where the leaves go?
Who can say, who can know, Where my days go?

Who can say, who can know, Where the leaves go?
Who can say, who can know, Where my days go?

[1] This is a song of healing and is sung over and over by the medicine man.

Gypsy Song

Marchette Gaylord Chute

Hungarian Folk Tune

1. When I grow to be a man,
2. I would have a lit - tle horse;
3. In my jour - ney I'd go past

I should like to trav - el With a gyp - sy
Through the hills I'd ride him. Ev - 'ry night I
Won - ders ev - 'ry min - ute; If I grow up

car - a - van, O - ver grass and grav - el.
would, of course, Go to sleep be - side him.
ver - y fast Then I can be - gin it.

The Lonely Song

Nancy Byrd Turner

Austrian Folk Tune

Simply

1. The woods are deep and still, (cuck-oo!)
2. Who sings that song a - lone, (cuck-oo!)

No wind is on the hill; (cuck-oo!)
That call with sil - ver tone? (cuck-oo!)

And in all the air a - round, (cuck-oo!)
'Tis a far - off hid - den bird, (cuck-oo!)

There is one clear, lone - ly sound. (cuck-oo!)
With a sin - gle, jin - gle word. (cuck-oo!)

And in all the air a - round, (cuck-oo!)
'Tis a far - off hid - den bird, (cuck-oo!)

There is one clear, lone-ly sound. (cuck-oo, cuck-oo!)
With a sin - gle, jin - gle word. (cuck-oo, cuck-oo!)

Tree Town

ROTE

Louise Ayres Garnett   Austrian Folk Tune

1. There's a large ma-ple tree where the birds like to be;
2. In the house I like best,—do not call it a nest!—

It's a town with some hous-es and a green branch-ing street.
Moth - er Bird sits all day be-fore her wide o - pen door,

You should see how the birds with man-y twit-ter-ing words
Quite con-tent-ed to wait un-til she spies through the gate

Get a-talk-ing while a-walk-ing as they hap-pen to meet.
All the good things Fa-ther Bird brings from the gro-cer-y store.

A Surprise

Rose Fyleman

Polish Folk Tune

Happily

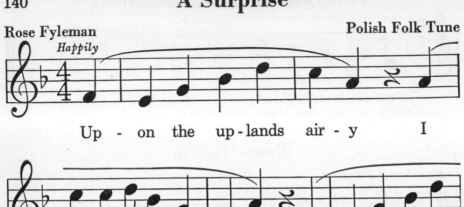

Up - on the up - lands air - y   I

spied such a ti - ny fair - y;   Po - lite - ly did I

greet her   And said I was pleased to meet her.   She

smiled up - on me sweet - ly, Then dis - ap - peared quite com-

plete - ly.   I   saw the dew - drops gleam - ing;

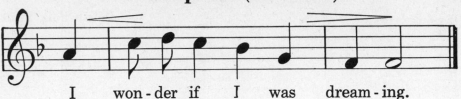

I won-der if I was dream-ing.

The Dance

Louise Ayres Garnett — Yugoslavian Folk Tune

Merrily

1. The mu-sic is play-ing, The danc-ers are seen.
2. Will you be my part-ner And give me this dance?

They swing all a-round, swing all a-round,
Count one, two, and three, one, two, and three!

Then give a bound spright-ly And tap on the ground
I seem to be hop-ping; So you will a - gree

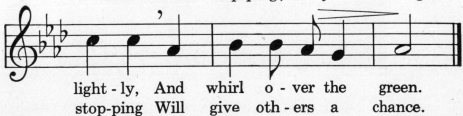

light - ly, And whirl o - ver the green.
stop-ping Will give oth - ers a chance.

3

Girl with Cat

Painted by the German artist PAUL HOECKER, in 1887

The Girl with the Cat

ROTE

Mabel Livingstone

Mana-Zucca

With expression

I have a lit - tle kit - ty, I'm

ver - y fond of her; · I give her milk and

crack - ers, And stroke her silk - y fur. · We

sit be - fore the fire, · She sleeps up-on · my knee. I'm

ver - y fond of kit - ty And kit-ty is fond of me.

Nine Red Horsemen

Eleanor Farjeon   **Mexican Folk Tune**

1. I · saw nine red horse - men
2. Their · hair streamed be - hind them,
3. Their · spurs clinked and jin - gled,

Rid - ing o - ver the plain,
And their eyes were a - shine;
And their laugh - ter was gay,

And · each held his charg - er
They · all rode as one man,
And · in the red sun - set

By its long flow - ing mane.
Though I knew there were nine.
They all gal - loped a - way.

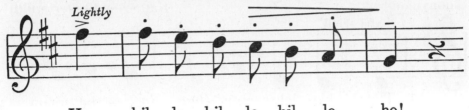

Lightly

Ho hil - lo, hil - lo, hil - lo ho!

Ho hil - lo, hil - lo, hil - lo ho!

Ho hil - lo, hil - lo, hil - lo ho!

Ho hil - lo, hil - lo, hil - lo ho!

The Red Apple

Anonymous

Katharine Conley Smith

In playful spirit

1. The big sky - man that makes the moon
2. To - day I went to get that moon;

Put one in our ap - ple tree.
I climbed up the ap - ple tree.

I saw it when I went to bed;
The moon was gone, but in its stead

The tree was black, the moon was red,
I found an ap - ple round and red,

And round as round could be.
And nice as nice could be.

Mistress Mary

Mother Goose

Mary B. Black

Playfully

Mis - tress Ma - ry, quite con - tra - ry,

How does your gar - den grow?

With sil - ver bells and cock - le - shells

And pret - ty maids all in a row, row, row,

With pret - ty maids all in a row. · ·

Daisies

ROTE

Frank Dempster Sherman

G. A. Grant-Schaefer

Smoothly, with feeling

1. At eve-ning when I go to bed I
3. For when at morn-ing I a - rise, There's

see the stars shine o-ver-head; They are the lit - tle
not a star left in the skies; She's picked them all and

dai - sies white That dot the mead-ow of the
dropped them down In - to the mead-ows of the

Fine   *A little faster*

night.   2. And of-ten while I'm dream-ing so, A -
town.

cross the sky the moon will go; It is a la - dy,

Daisies (*Continued*)

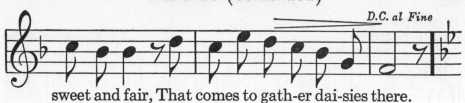

D.C. al Fine

sweet and fair, That comes to gath-er dai-sies there.

Signs of Spring

Nellie Poorman   Bohemian Folk Tune

Happily

1. Come with your skip-ping rope, jack-stones, and a ball!
2. Bring out your mar-bles and make a mer-ry ring;

May-time is   here a - gain, heed her hap-py call.
Roll - er skates, spin-ning tops, kite up-on   a string.

What a love-ly   day for frol - ic and for play!
Ev-'ry-thing is   gay, come quick-ly and o - bey

Her   gift   to   you   all.
This   glad   call   of   spring.

The Orchard

Translated by
Cecil Cowdrey

Swedish Folk Song

When white ap-ple-blos-soms crowd on their branch-es so fair,

'Tis said that the an-gels gath-er to watch o'er them there.

And when I lie a - dream-ing 'neath the

great ap - ple tree, I think there in the

si - lence they are sing - ing to me.

My Garden

Ethel H. Tewksbury

R. T. Bjorkman

Happily

1. With a spade and rake and hoe,
2. Seeds are plant - ed in a row,

To my gar - den I will go;
Soon they will be - gin to grow;

It is read - y for me to sow
Work! or may - be you'll nev - er know

My Garden (*Continued*)

What - ev - er   I   like   best.
How   nice   it   is   to   rest.

Cheerio

ROTE

Melba Knaus Loughlin   Melba Knaus Loughlin

Merrily

"Cheer - i - o,   cheer - i - o! Chir-rup,   chir-rup!"

That's what the rob - in · sings to · me.

"Cheer - i - o,   cheer - i - o! Chir-rup,   chir-rup!"

Oh,   how hap - py   he   must   be!

Singing

Robert Louis Stevenson

Newton Swift

1. Of speck-led eggs the · bird-ie sings
2. The chil-dren sing in · far Ja-pan;

And nests a-mong the trees;
The chil-dren sing in Spain;

The sail-or sings of ropes and things
The or-gan with the or-gan man

In ships up-on the seas. ·
Is sing-ing · in the

rain, · Is sing-ing, sing-ing in the rain.

The Game

Susanna Myers

German Folk Tune

1. A - round and round and round we go,
2. A - round and round a - gain we go,

March - ing in a sin - gle row;
March - ing in a dou - ble row;

To keep in step we al - ways try;
Our flags are fly - ing high and proud,

We wheel and turn in pass - ing by
Our drums are beat - ing clear and loud;

Where John, up-on a plat-form high, calls out our names.
Then John, up-on the plat-form there, calls out our names.

The Wind

Clara Edwards   Clara Edwards

Smoothly and sweetly

1. Woo - oo,   woo - oo,   woo - oo,   woo - oo.
2. H'mm,   h'mm,   h'mm,   h'mm.

Hear   the   wind!   It   loud - ly   blows;
Now   it   sings   some   lull - a - bies

Cov - er   up   the   ba - by's   toes;
While   the   dark   comes   o'er   the   skies;

It   may   bite   them   as   it   goes.
Time   to   close   all   sleep - y   eyes.

Very soft

Woo - oo,   woo - oo,   woo - oo,   woo - oo.
H'mm,   h'mm,   h'mm,   h'mm.

Cobwebs

The Rabbit

ROTE

Edith King

Mary Root Kern

Brightly

1. Brown bun - ny sits · in - side his bur-row
2. He nib - bles all · a - bout the bush-es,
3. You see some lit - tle streaks and flash-es

Till ev - 'ry - thing is still; ·
Or sits to wash his face; ·
And then a twink of white, ·

Then out he slips a - long the fur-row.
But at a sound he stamps and rush - es
As down his hid - y hole he dash - es

Or up the grass - y hill. ·
With quite sur - pris - ing pace. ·
And dis - ap - pears from sight. ·

The Santa Fe Trail

Christine Turner Curtis

Theo Halle

Steadily, with well-marked rhythm

1. Plod a-long, plod, on the San-ta Fe Trail;
2. Plod a-long, plod, on the San-ta Fe Trail;

Plod a-long, plod, on the San-ta Fe Trail.
Plod a-long, plod, on the San-ta Fe Trail.

Oh, the des-ert sun is bold, And the
Oh, the des-ert dawn is rose, And a-

des-ert nights are cold. On we plod through
head are moun-tain snows. Ox-en pant and

chok-ing sand, Cac-tus, sage on ei-ther hand, O-ver
wag-ons sway. Now for wa-ter loud we pray, As the

The Santa Fe Trail (*Continued*)

bare and burn - ing land. Oh, the wea - ry des - ert
dust rolls thick and gray. Oh, the des - ert sun sets

wide! And the In - dians watch us ride.
clear, And the sil - ver stars draw near.

The Santa Fe Trail

Painted by the Scottish artist JOHN YOUNG-HUNTER, and now in a private collection

Clap and Click

Louise Ayres Garnett   Russian Folk Tune

With spirit

1. Clap, clap your hands to-geth-er, clap them light-ly!
2. Click, click your heels to-geth-er, click them loud-ly!

Snap, snap your fin-gers this way, like a whip!
There's noth-ing half so jol - ly as this noise.

Bow to your right and left po - lite - ly,
Now stamp your feet and stamp them proud - ly,

Whirl-ing a - bout, your hand on your hip.
Whirl-ing a - gain, first girls and then boys.

Clap, clap your hands to-geth - er, clap them light-ly!
Click, click your heels to-geth - er, click them loud-ly!

Clap and Click *(Continued)*

Snap, snap your fin-gers this way, like a whip!
There's noth-ing half so jol - ly as this noise.

Let's Play

Mary C. Gleitz

Polish Folk Tune

Not too fast

1. Come, have a store with me
2. We'll have some cake to sell,
3. Each one will take a turn;

Un - der the ap - ple tree! I'll bring the
Crack-ers and tea as well. We'll need some
We'll see how much we earn. Then when our

coun-ter board, You bring some bits of cord.
mon-ey too; But - tons will have to do.
play is through, I will di - vide with you.

3

Shadows

ROTE

Mary C. Gleitz   Norwegian Folk Tune

Lightly and smoothly

1. Now the sun is shin - ing,
2. I will go and see, now,

So bright - ly, light - ly shin - ing;
Just where the dark may be, now;

I should like so well to know,
Some is there be - hind a wall,

Where does all the dark - ness go
Some be - hind the hous - es tall;

When the sun is shin - ing?
Come and look with me, now!

Vacation Days

Nellie Poorman   Spanish Folk Tune

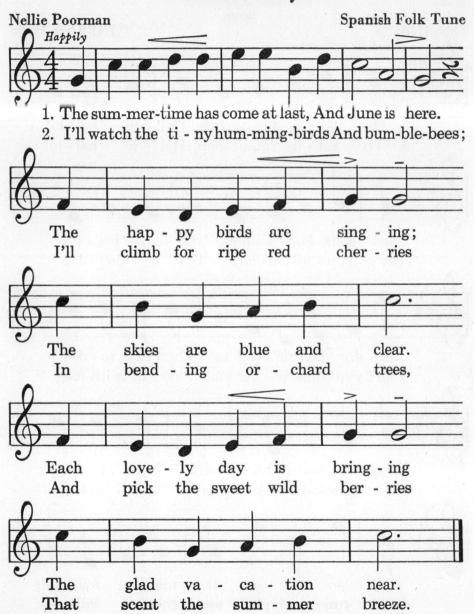

1. The sum-mer-time has come at last, And June is here.
2. I'll watch the ti - ny hum-ming-birds And bum-ble-bees;

The   hap - py   birds   arc   sing - ing;
I'll   climb for   ripe   red   cher - ries

The   skies are   blue   and   clear.
In   bend - ing   or - chard   trees,

Each   love - ly   day   is   bring - ing
And   pick   the sweet wild   ber - ries

The   glad   va - ca - tion   near.
That   scent the sum - mer   breeze.

The Telephone Call

ROTE

Theo Halle

Theo Halle

Gracefully, with expression

1. The tel - e - phone rings! Hel - lo, hel - lo!
2. 'Tis Bil - lie and Joan, Hel - lo, hel - lo!

And some-bod - y sings, "Hel - lo, hel - lo!"
They're home all a - lone; Hel - lo, hel - lo!

Who do you think will be phon-ing to - day?
"Can't you come o - ver and vis - it with me?

What do you think he will have to say?
I have some cook - ies and cam - bric tea."

I'll go and see; it may be for me;
We'll run and play and then I will say,

And then I'll know who is call - ing.
"I thank you, Bil - lie, for call - ing."

The Lamps of Night

Louise Ayres Garnett   English Folk Tune

Happily

1. The lamps of night are the stars a - light,
2. The lamps by day fade and go a - way

And they spar - kle white and clear;
With the oth - er things of night;

And as they gleam, lit - tle stars will al - ways seem
Yet there they are; ev - 'ry ti - ny lit - tle star

Like some - bod - y's chan - de - lier.
Keeps glim - mer - ing out of sight.

The Kite

Mary C. Gleitz
Czechoslovakian Folk Tune

Lightly and gracefully

1. Tra la la! Tra la la! All of us to-geth-er,
2. Tra la la! Tra la la! How the strings are cross-ing!

Fly-ing our kites in this ver-y wind-y weath-er.
High in the sun-light the frisk-y tails are toss-ing.

See how they sail in the ver-y wind-y weath-er!
See how the kites in the mer-ry wind are toss-ing!

At the Fair

Hope Ann Rhodes

Lettish Folk Tune

1. At the fair, all your friends are there, And the
2. Please de - cide if you'd like to ride! You may

fly - ing hors - es gay - ly are pranc-ing
catch the ring as swift - ly you're fly - ing

Round and round, with a mer - ry sound;
Round and round, with a mer - ry sound;

Bet - ter fun nev - er will be found.
Bet - ter fun nev - er will be found.

Swimming

ROTE

Carol Fuller

Finnish Folk Tune

With graceful rhythm

1. Oh, come, we're go - ing swim - ming!
2. Now duck your head way un - der,

So bring your dog a - long too; The
And try to learn how to float! Don't

suit I wore last sum - mer Will ver - y near-ly fit
shout and swal-low wa - ter; It's ver - y bad for your

you. I'll let you use my bath-ing shoes As
throat. And if a frog should bite your toes, Don't

long as you can stay; Come on, we're go - ing
fright - en him a - way! Come on, we're go - ing

swim - ming! We'll play in the pond all   day.
swim - ming! We'll play in the pond all   day.

Morning Prayer

Jane Beecham   Edward J. Hopkins

With reverence

1. Our   Fa - ther, kind and   strong
2. Help   us   to   wor - ship   Thee

And   watch - ful   of   us   all,
In   thought and serv - ice,   too;

We   wor - ship Thee in   pray'r and song,
Un -   self - ish may   we   al - ways be,

Thy   chil - dren, great and   small.
To   Thee and friends be   true.

With Happy Voices

Marjorie Knapp

Ethelbert W. Bullinger

With sustained tone

1. Fa-ther, with hap-py voic-es we're sing-ing
2. Fa-ther, with qui-et hearts we are pray-ing,

Thanks for cool-ness and rain,
Ask-ing Thee for Thy care;

And all the joy the show-ers are bring-ing,
We would be strong to work, and in play-ing

Then sun-shine a-gain.
Be kind-ly and fair.

America

ROTE

S. F. Smith

Henry Carey

With spirit

1. My coun - try! 'tis of thee, Sweet land
2. My na - tive coun - try, thee, Land of
3. Let mu - sic swell the breeze, And ring
4. Our fa - thers' God! to Thee, Au - thor

of lib - er - ty, Of thee I sing; Land where my
the no - ble free, Thy name I love; I love thy
from all the trees Sweet free - dom's song; Let mor - tal
of lib - er - ty, To Thee we sing; Long may our

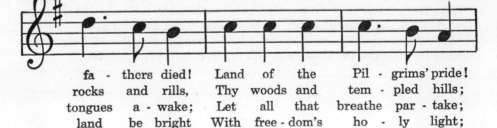

fa - thers died! Land of the Pil - grims' pride!
rocks and rills, Thy woods and tem - pled hills;
tongues a - wake; Let all that breathe par - take;
land be bright With free - dom's ho - ly light;

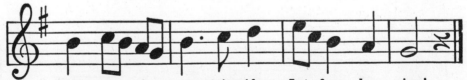

From ev - 'ry moun - tain side, Let free - dom ring!
My heart with rap - ture thrills Like that a - bove.
Let rocks their sil - lence break, The sound pro - long.
Pro - tect us by Thy might, Great God, our King!

Acknowledgments

THE EDITORS ARE UNDER DEEP OBLIGATION TO MR. E. W. NEWTON
FOR HIS VALUABLE SERVICE, WISE COUNSEL, AND ABLE LEADERSHIP

Acknowledgment is due also to Mr. Ennis D. Davis for assistance in establishing contacts with folk-song collectors in Europe and America; to Charles Scribner's Sons for permission to use the poem "Rock-a-by" by J. G. Holland and the poem "Singing" by Robert Louis Stevenson; to D. Appleton-Century Company for the poem "The Rabbit" by Edith King, from *Fifty New Poems for Children*, and to this publisher and the author for the poem "Merry-go-round" by Mabel Livingstone, from *St. Nicholas*; for the poem "Uncle Frank," from *Goose Grass Rimes* by Monica Shannon, copyright 1930 by Doubleday, Doran and Company, Inc.; for the poem "Daisies" by Frank Dempster Sherman, used by permission of and by arrangement with Houghton Mifflin Company; for the poem "Indian Lullaby" by Charles Myall, used by permission of Mrs. Sarah A. Graham, owner of the copyright; for the Jamaican tune on page 65, from *Jamaican Folklore*, used by permission of the American Folklore Society; for the Finnish tune on page 108, from *Das Lied der Völker*, Volume III, used by permission of B. Schott's Söhne, Mainz, Germany; and for two songs by Victor Young, "There Was a Goose" and "Young Mr. Duck," published by Schroeder and Gunther, Inc. The original illustrations are by Maud and Miska Petersham.

The editors appreciate the services of Louise Krueger and Harold Rugg in arranging the integration of these songs with the other curriculum subjects.

Alphabetical Index

173

174 Alphabetical Index

Alphabetical Index

175

176   Alphabetical Index